Leaving Traces

Nick Gerrard

Published by Nick Gerrard, 2024.

LEAVING TRACES

First edition. May 22, 2024.

ISBN: 979-8227197085

Written by Nick Gerrard.

Thanks to Helen Baggot for ediitng.

This is for my son Joe, so he knows.

Never having seen the Sun

The tower stands still; a ghost-like figure on the hill, a monument to the past. The wheel no longer turns; the coal wagons are left standing in a row still and rusting like the men that used to push them.

***

We met in the Old Bull and Bush. A pub we had drunk in during the Great strike. Whenever miners and supporters came to the support group meetings in the union club we would go there after for some beers and some laughs and lengthy debates about politics. So, it seemed the right place to meet up again. She was in town to do a talk...twenty-five years after the strike. There was to be a showing of a documentary then various veterans of the dispute would chat. I was going to the meeting but wanted to have a more personal meet up.

I felt a bit embarrassed that we hadn't seen each other for such a long time; felt I had let her down somewhat. But after the strike ended lots of friends never saw each other again. We all went in different directions; all followed different paths.

I got a beer and sat in a corner booth. After five minutes I saw her come in. Still had a perm and now was wearing some blue stylish glasses. She looked well. We hugged closely, for a long time, we didn't speak for a while; we just smiled and wiped our eyes.

We had a few drinks and a quick chat about her family and mine and then I followed her in to hear her talk.

After a few celebs she took to the stage.

'We walked back to work with our men, with our heads held high. We had lost the dispute but we felt like not the battle. We knew now that our battle was for life.

'Most of us women would never go back to how things were, I mean some did, became the same put upon housewives they had been before but a lot of us could never go back.

1

'And I think our husbands had changed too, they respected us more now, for what we did at home with the kids and keeping the house but also for the things we had done in the strike. We had formed food kitchens, we went on pickets, we collected money and toys for the kids, we made sure everyone was taken care of, the old people in need of a bucket or two of coal, the mum feeling depressed.

'And then we grew. We wrote poetry, we put on plays, we sang, we drew. We provided outlets for women that had never been there before.

'Don't get me wrong, the main thing was that we supported our men in their fight, against Thatcher and the state.

'To them we were the enemy, on TV at night I saw me portrayed as an evil communist, a scourge on the nation. But I was just an ordinary working-class woman, my man an ordinary hard-working man. What we wanted was to be able to work and keep our communities.

'I had never thought about politics before, never watched the news, but during the strike I realised that everything was politics, our whole lives were political. We met other women from different class backgrounds, women involved in women's rights, CND and solidarity campaigns for other women, struggling around the world.

'And we learnt a lot from these women. We went to support the women camped out at the American bases; we collected money for women in Nicaragua fighting for a new society. We went to meetings and listened to these women, and I think we took what they said back with us and used their inspiration to be political and active in our own right.

'Our solidarity fed the strikers, got presents for Christmas for the kids; our actions got support and money for the dispute. And our actions got us beaten, and arrested and the more they did this the more determined we became.'

I looked around as the hall clapped and hollered.

She took a breath, a step back and took in the applause but without a smile. She stepped forward again.

'But our fight hasn't ended. It never ended when the men went back to work. Eventually the pits were closed, as the union and Arthur had said they would be. And our biggest fight began.

'Now, our men were on the dole, stuck at home, some days they just sat in front of the telly sinking in the mire, some days they couldn't be bothered to dress. And some drank, in the miners' social clubs that the women kept running, the men sat and drank too much.

'And our kids started to get into more trouble than usual. The conflict in the homes was toxic to the kids. They didn't look up to their dads anymore and never listened to us. And the constant fighting between husband and wife is not good for them. And suddenly drugs began to appear.

Funny that, the mines closed and heroin suddenly appeared in vast quantities, replacing the coal. Some men got other jobs, but not good jobs; driving vans, working in electronic parts factories. There were no unions and the pay was bad, but it was something.

'But, the spirit had gone from most of them. Not all of them, some are still political, still keep the spirit of the union going, even if it's just blowing their bloody trumpets!

'But we women stepped up, our fight never ended; now we had our men to kick up the arse and get to put the pint down. Our kids to smack round the head after they smashed up a bus shelter or beaten up a small kid.

'And our community centres became help centres. We set up AA meeting groups, but also we tried to provide some social activities, from practice space for would-be rock stars to the old brass bands still blowing along. And we had to get funding for these things, we had to coordinate and organise like we had during the strike...

'We got professionals in to help with isolated depressed women and men, we have raffles and sing-song nights and I think we managed to keep our community together and positive.

'Like I said our fight never ended.

'And we are still political; we support any worthwhile cause, any strikers fighting for their jobs, any community fighting to survive.

'We women keep each other positive, we are all political and determined. The union has gone but not the spirit; it still exists in our community activities.

'But that may sound all nice and cosy like, and maybe I have painted a bright picture when I shouldn't have, because what we are most involved in, day to day is trying to get our kids off the gear.

'Our community centres are heroin support centres. We get medical help when we can and try and keep the kids off with support. But it's not easy...what can we offer them? No university, zero-hour contract jobs in some crappy warehouse, not much of a future.

'They look at their dads drinking themselves to death and do the same with heroin. Maybe our work can inspire them, it inspires other women we know but the men; it's harder.

'We need more jobs and opportunities for the kids, more college spaces, more proper jobs. And if I am asking for anything tonight, from you trade unionists, you labour supporters, you campaigners; it is this. We need to fight for a better society, better jobs, better education, proper wages and unions. The same things we needed a hundred years ago.

'We are still fighting, the miners' wives, we ask you to do the same, for the next generation and the ones to come.'

Everyone stood and cheered, she held her hand aloft in a clenched fist and we sang 'Coal not Dole'. Most of us took the pieces of paper with the words on; we had forgotten a lot of them.

'What will become of this pit-yard where men once trampled faces hard?'

The tears ran down my cheeks.

'So tired and weary their shift done, never having seen the sun.'

The Stranger of Gdansk

You saw him early morning most days. Black trilby, black mid-length woollen coat, scuffed brogues and thread-bare baggy suit trousers; he always had that grey suit on under the coat. Always the same red tie and smudged cream collar shirts. The stranger we called him. No one knew his name or where he came from. I said good day to him and he half smiled back. He passed my art stall outside the café Gunter Grass on his way to the bakers over the bridge, at the back of the waterfront. On his way back he passed under the archway and watched the busking cellists; especially if they played his favourite Bella Ciao. Then with his bag of rolls or poppy-seed cakes he took a table outside Schulz's café. He drank his coffee short and smoked his cigarettes long; both strong and black. He passed me and turned into Krzywe Street, typed in his key to the iron gate and went inside and climbed the stairs to the small attic room, Mrs Brzozowa had told us he inhabited.

Same every day; the stranger. He interested us, the waiters, the painters, the store keepers. Maybe because he was a criminal? An escapee? We didn't know and so he interested us, and he kept himself to himself and was civil so that was about all we could expect.

I say this happened most days, but sometimes he would not appear, or disappear for a couple of weeks. Then we would spot him again, during his morning routine or on his afternoon one. He was creature of habit, this we knew.

About 2pm every day he went to the market and picked up apples or cherries and sometimes French beans and walnuts. 2pm was a good time to go to the market, the morning buyers, always in a rush and ready to spend money on bad produce had gone; and the people who shopped in the afternoon could pick the best bits.

We wondered if he cooked but thought perhaps that he didn't. He stopped off at the delicatessen for a salami and a nice fresh cheese, sometimes some sausage or a jar of duck confit.

Every three days or so, we thought when he had run out of sausage and, he went down the fisherman's wharf, to the fisherman's café, or a fresh fish; whatever was in season, and a carafe of red wine, never white, always red, never mind the fish.

His routine only changed in winter; in the café in the early morning and the fish café in the early evening, by him getting a table in the corner inside and putting up the collar of his woollen coat and pulling his hat down slightly on his walk home.

We wondered about this man and felt sorry for him. He was alone, we worried that he was lonely; we wondered if we could help him somehow. How? We weren't sure.

One thing we knew was that he liked words! I mean, he loved to read. He always had newspapers, what looked like foreign ones too; which he sometimes huffed at. And if not newspapers always a tatty paperback, which he sometimes chuckled at.

And he wrote; what? We knew not. But he scribbled as if it was a race. In school-kid notebooks. All of a sudden he would take one out of his inside pocket urgently and scribble frantically, sometimes for thirty minutes without looking up. Then he would stop, look, grin and put it back inside.

The only other thing the stranger did was walk the shore line, inspecting the ships newly in, with his hands behind his back. And then would converse with a ship hand, in a variety of languages. My friends would report to me.

-Today he was down the docks, speaking Italian like a native!
Or.
-Yeah Russian or something like that!
Even.

-As sure as I am standing here I swear he was rabbiting on in Arabic, full spittle!

And then he was gone.

Mrs Brzozowa said he paid a month's rent and packed his few things in a tatty brown case and bid her farewell.

Just like that. No reason given. No explanation offered. No goodbyes or see-you-agains. Gone.

And we forgot about him. What was there to remember him for really?

And then it appeared, almost a year since his leaving.

It was for sale in the bookshops.

The Gawpers of Gdansk.

A short book, but we were all in there.

'The man at the art shop, always saying hello, but wanting more.'

'The waitress in the café wanting to know what I had been up to.'

'The old men by the docks, keeping an eye on me, watching who I talked to.'

'They thought I didn't know that they traded information of my daily routine. The vegetable salesman reported to the landlady, who reported to the artist, who reported to the waiters; and so on.'

'No one offered me real friendship, they only offered their ears to gossip.'

'A neighbourhood of nosey parkers, busy bodies and Kibitzers!'

And people bought the book, and our neighbours laughed when we passed and tourists started to look for us, and we stood fake grinning as families posed with us for selfies. All these strangers!

The Men on the Hot Prague Roof

Yesterday, what if you hadn't walked to the metro,
       past the graffiti and piss stained corners,
       past the beggar with his head down and his bowl out.

What if you hadn't stood packed like a fish whiffing old socks and garlic in the 5am rush.

What if your missis hadn't packed you some rolls and smoked mackerel spread with whitey green pepper slices.

What if you hadn't stopped at the newspaper stand and had a shot of Slivovice with your sports paper.

What if you hadn't got to the site at six and met the other guys; all with a range of moods and some degree of a hangover.

What if you hadn't taken the temporary rickety lift up to the top of the building and took a deep breath before looking out over Vinohrady at the expanse and red roofs of Prague.

What if you hadn't mixed that first batch of concrete and started laying those bricks like de Vinci. What if you hadn't taken off your shirt at ten after sweating out last night's beer.

What if that temperature gauge hadn't reached 30 before 12.

What if you and the guys had said, *Enough!*

What if you come down off that Saharan roof and gone for a cool one.

What if you hadn't stayed there...loading and unloading, lifting and dragging, the water trickling down your baked back.

What if you hadn't thought of Linda and the three kids at home in the rabbit hutch with no garden to blow a paddling pool up in.

What if you didn't have flimsy walls and no breeze and an unsheltered tiny balcony to go back to.

What if these beautiful apartments growing up nearer heaven were occupied by the old residents of Prague.

What if you could be building an apartment on a roof for *you*.

What if the people with money had left Prague alone.

What if *you* lived in the historic areas instead of the baristas and the artisan bakers.

What if the concept shops could be replaced by light-bulb shops.

What if you could afford a full lunch in the pub on the corner instead of rolls and plastic bottles of Fanta.

What if you had soup of the day followed by gulas and dumplings.

What if you didn't have to return to the top of the roof after a break in the shade next to the tram stop downstairs.

What if you could go home to a nice family house on the edges and relax with a beer with your feet on the summer table.

What if you said to the boss, *It's too hot to work!*

What if that turbo powered fan blasting the family lounging in the flat opposite were turned on you. What if at three you could rub oil in that leathered back.

What if you didn't have to go down to the Underground again and get squashed again and drips roll into your eyes.

What if just making it through the day wasn't enough.

What if you could make it without ever even trying.

What if you weren't leaving all your dreams behind.

What if you could just get a little ahead.

What if you hadn't left school at an early age cuss you fucked about.

What if you had studied a bit more so you could be the guy in the office with the air conditioning. What if your building had different writing on the walls.

What if the neighbourhood playground had grass instead of sticky tar.

What if you and Linda had planned better.

What if the beer at the kiosk was in a glass not a bottle.

What if maybe on another day you'd stop crying.

What if you hadn't gambled and drank.

What if you hadn't gone behind her back; tonight you would be looking forward to something.

What if you still had dreams...you swig the bottle and think of old ones unfulfilled.

What if you had to do it all again...instead, you stand and drag your fag on the boiling roof.

What if the sun stopped beating and you could stand in the shade for a while.

Waiting for that door to open

'Medicine!'

We line up for our named plastic drug cups. Neck them quickly then line up again for our smokes.

Packets and lighters checked from the basket from the second drawer down.

I was the only one with an electric one; I fill it with liquid and check the battery. Ready to go.

I sneak to the toilet before they let us out; I smoke quickly to pre-empt the emptying of my bowels.

I need the nicotine but my body is still fucked up and my bowels move suddenly and violently.

I go back to the door, put on my coat and boots and wait for the reluctant nurse to turn the key.

Finally we are out.

My fellow patients place a chair for me to sit. I am still detoxing and too shaky to stand and the buzz of the nicotine makes me shake even more. I hold off the shits and the need to vomit. I take in as much as I can before I am too sick to take more. We are on the side of the old monastery and beautiful baroque buildings that now house a hospital, drink tank and psycho unit. The masonry work is beautiful. We stand on the top with majestic staircases either side of our place. Down below are gardens and a scout hut in a corner, then fields and factories and the railway yards. I smile and try to think good thoughts for a second but then my sickness returns and I can no longer smoke, I get up and wobble, am helped inside as the smokers frantically light another fag. I stagger to the toilet and shit painfully, then lie down and wait for the dizziness to pass.

This is my second day here. Three times a day this happens; it's not enough. Three times a day after meals and drugs; we all need more nicotine than this. Shit we are all in long term recovery from alcohol.

I had come here after the one night of hell in the drink tank via the intense psycho ward. Before that I had had three weeks of non-stop vodka, three-hourly trips to the 24-hour shop, then a head wound and stitches, screaming, fighting and eventually hospitalisation. I took the short sharp shock of the drink tank, to get my alcohol level down to zero so that I could get the drugs to help with the withdrawals.

The drink tank...one night of being strapped to a bed; tied to your bad trip, your shakes. Unable to escape the screams and shouts of madmen; the stench, the vomit, the crying.

You wait in the morning to be checked and hopefully to God to be let out. A doctor came to check me; he remembered me from the last time.

-You are going straight to the unit right?

-I hope so, doc.

He took pity on me and got a nurse to inject diazepam into my arse. It helped me a little. I got my stuff together...I couldn't check if I had everything as I didn't remember what I came with.

The ambulance took me to the unit. I hung around with my wife; signing forms, vomiting.

We chatted to another doctor... 'Give me drugs now...please.' He was helpful and did, and it helped for a while.

I am admitted, given ill-fitting pyjamas and too big plastic slippers, and then I am tested and prodded and thankfully given more drugs. I try and sleep but only doze, and then I feel bad again and start the pacing.

I pace to pass the time in between drug out-givings. I pace to stop from thinking, I pace to stay sane.

I am given food, but don't eat, I drink thin tea and pace and wait for drugs to get me better.

Three days I pace...I am then transferred here to the long-term alcohol place, the baroque asylum.

The drugs here are better, stronger, but we have to do therapy sessions...everyone here has been here a while and has stopped withdrawing...I am still fucked. I skip as many therapy sessions as possible...the physical exercises in the morning, the group talking; the meditation...the doctors get angry but I don't care, the nurses get mean, but I don't care.

Every morning the early shift nurses wake me up.

-Good morning, let's go, arses out of bed!

Loudly and bangily. I know that's not a real word but Jesus it really describes how they wake us up. I could have put a swoosh here to signify the sweep of the curtains. But that's not how the early morning shift nurses do it; they bang them open, and then bang everything; your clothes off the floor onto the chair, your fresh water jug onto your bedside rig. Then they go about their tasks with swift efficiency.

Toilets are being mopped as the waking dead stagger to pee, to brush and just to shuffle; up and down the corridor, waiting to be fed meds.

Little white plastic drug jugs checked next to long lists of names, and what pharmaceuticals go with each patient. Blood pressures taken, beds stripped; new patients stripped. All smart and military-like fashion.

-Sleep OK?

-How you feeling today, Mr Clarke?

-Look at this rain!

Friendly, unsmiling but friendly, and busy. Breakfast to get done.

It's 6.30 in the morning and the factory is up and running.

I drag my hard stripped hospital issue baggy pajamaed arse to the toilet, then shuffle along with the rest of 'um.

-Morning.

-Yes.

-Huh!

-Good day!

The actor is sullen today, just a grunt.

The hippy kid smiley, but silent.

The baroness is yet to appear, she needs to put on her face.

The doors to three rooms are half closed to hide terrors.

We all look for glimpses as we drag past.

A body inside a netted cage, another strapped down, another in a corner trying to disappear into the wall.

I stand and wait for the door to open and to drag.

Fruitcake Sandwiches

When I was a kid I was into lots of things; football, cricket, Bruce Lee, listening to old sixties 45s; and other things which came and went, waxing and waning with my attention span. Like any normal little kid, I think.

But, two things I stayed into and were the most important things in my life: football and food. The football I got from my granddad; almost as soon as I could walk I was kicking a ball and my greatest thrill was going to the stadium every two weeks and supporting our team. Every spare minute I had I was outside kicking a ball; in summer we were into cricket too but football was our first love.

My love of food came from my nan and my mum who both worked in the trade and both had a love for good food. I never thought of it as being that special when I was a kid, it was kind of normal to like good food, why would you like shit food? It was only later on that I realised how much I loved food, the cooking, the buying and the eating of it.

My nan worked at a posh café in one of the old Victorian arcades in the centre of Brum. She wore the classic waitress gear and we could only go in and visit if we wore our Sunday best. This didn't happen very often but once in a while my mum got dolled up and we got scrubbed and we went for tea. The counter was filled with fresh cream cakes, my favourite were the chocolate éclairs with golden fresh cream and proper chocolate. And I had milkshake or even an ice cream soda which was like a taste of heaven. My mum usually had scones with butter and cream and jam and a frothy coffee that I loved the sound it made; conjured up by the white-shirted black-tied man behind the counter, hidden in a cloud of steam and swooshing noises.

As I said we didn't go there often but my nan bought loads of broken or unsold cakes home with her which we thought was the height of luxury.

15

Then my nan moved to the Chamber of Commerce offices which had a huge kitchen and restaurant and only cooked lunches. I would go there a couple of times a week to meet her at the end of her shift and when I entered those kitchens it was a world of wonder for me. The smells, the shouting, the characters. There were a bunch of cooks and chefs from all over the world, all with their tall hats and fat bellies. And they would grab me, swing me round, pinch my cheeks and get me to eat.

'Hey Nick, taste this duck!'

'Nick, sit down try the dessert!' The food was good, English and fancy French, and I tasted it all and loved it all. But my favourite thing there was the just baked fresh rolls right from the oven.

At home we had good food too. My nan was a great cook. She baked a lot; cakes and fresh bread, which we always tasted hot with yellow butter or fresh beef dripping. Her food wasn't fancy but she and my granddad went down to the rag market every few days to buy the best lamb chops, the freshest apples, the most succulent fish they could get. They always went near the end of the day when the butchers auctioned off stuff that was left over.

My granddad loved to get a bargain. He also loved to eat. A roast of any kind was his favourite but lamb chops he adored. Nothing was better for him than picking up the bones and nibbling away until they were stripped bare; and after he wiped the grease into his hands and spread it over his face. When I tried to do this my mum thumped the back of my head! But he got away with it. 'When no one's looking do it! It's great for your skin.'

We loved our burgers and hot dogs at the football too, and on Saturday morning before the game we went down to the butcher to get fresh friend pork scratchings, to eat later in front of the TV.

My granddad ate some weird stuff too; one of his favourites was a fruitcake in between two slices cut from a newly baked crusty cottage loaf with lashing of butter.

'Nothing better in this world!'

And he had a passion for scrumping fruit and veg. Whenever we visited the countryside he always took off with me in tow to highjack some farmer's field; didn't matter what. Could be apples could be sprouts.

'Nothing tastes quite so good as stolen food!'

My mum tells the story of how my granddad became known as the ice-cream man. He worked at the dairy, where he made the milk-floats that delivered dairy goods to various estates. He would nick a block of ice cream and come down the road with it encased in dry ice on the back of his bike. The kids would spot him coming and drop their balls and hula-hoops and go running to Uncle George, and stand in a perfect line to get a free slice of delight.

My mum was into her food too and worked as a waitress. Sometimes when she couldn't get a babysitter she took us along to some big hotel where we sat in the ladies' toilets or staff room, while the women stripped and swore and laughed their heads off. For a young boy just discovering the delights of the female this was like being allowed into a forbidden kingdom. They thought I was too small to be bothered with bare boobs and stockinged legs. I wasn't. And we got fed there too...the waitresses brought roast beef and potatoes and we dipped into terrines of gravy and then ate wedding cake and ice cream.

After school I worked in my uncle's café with my nan for a while, where I learnt to cook: apple crumbles, fish and chips, pasties; all great British food.

Then I got a job in a hotel and got French trained. After working in loads of restaurants in the UK my dream came true and I moved to Paris. I still live there and work in a cool restaurant making French and modern British dishes. And I love the French's appreciation of food and adore sitting outside a French café watching the world go by with a coffee and a croque-monsieur or a slice of cheese cake or flan. But still when I can get hold of a fruitcake sometimes I create the sandwich again, eaten with relish and nostalgia!

Out of her depth

As I left the Underground, I stood rigid for a second. This is not my kind of place at all! Look at all these weirdoes!

I gathered myself and pushed on.

I weaved in and out of the Spanish backpackers, the casual observers, the falafel eaters; the so-called beautiful people. My heart was missing beats.

I was away from the cosiness of my town. Away from the girls' nights out; the constant exchange of boyfriends. The comfort of endless, meaningless gossip. But it was my town and my life and I liked it that way!

The cramped bustling markets and stores, overflowed with Doc Martins, outrageous glasses, skimpy T-shirts. Retro in the alcoves, tourist trendy tat.

Drum and bass the soundtrack for jugglers, buskers, the masses of sheep herding up and down the high street.

Tarty, cheap. The words passed through my head, exiting at the turn of my nose, as I browsed the stalls.

Good-looking pierced girls posed, talking loudly. Which clubs were 'in', who was 'out'.

They showed little interest in their work. Occasionally swaggering over to groups of Japanese students.

They looked me up and down, turning their heads with sniffing sighs.

My secretarial black skirt was cut just above the knee. Smart but classy. My dangly earrings and bracelets were silver, but seemed cheap now, somehow.

In my small Midlands town, I was someone. Away from the dressing up in ya best and copping-off on a Friday night scene, I was viewed as an unfashionable straight girl.

Well, I was here! In London. In the 'happening areas' I'd read about.

Tourist infested, commercially over-run. The mainstream alternative.

I took a seat outside a Portuguese café, and ordered tea with milk.

The dark-skinned, sunken cheeked waiter, laid down the tea, and waited impatiently for payment. He was too busy to care. He was busy double side kissing and ciaoing a string of bear-bellied beauties.

I held my cigarette awkwardly, like I'd just started smoking that week.

What the hell was I doing here?

I'd met Trevor at one of those work 'dos'. Seminars for the new upwardly mobile working class.

The kids whose patched together families were put into the new towns in the seventies. The kids who'd done all right at school, then taken up the chancers' jobs at the end of the Thatcher years.

A little computer knowledge, a couple of O-levels; smart appearance, a willingness to get on.

Drive and want being rewarded with company cars, package holidays to Greece, gadgets and mortgages.

I had bought a house just down the road from me mum.

Bought it with Darren, a self-employed carpet fitter. Jealous type. Football on a Sunday morning. Out with the lads on a Friday, out with me on a Saturday.

Even in a curry house, Daz ordered chicken and chips.

Not like Trevor.

He'd impressed me when we'd first met. He'd even talked over dinner. About wine, travel, music, a bit of politics even; and only a smidgen of football.

But he had talked to me, and had asked me questions.

I had felt comfortable and excited. He hadn't tried to out think me, out do me; conquer. He listened.

He had liked my hair, and the smell of my perfume, he hadn't thought it too much.

We had talked and drank late into the night.

We had had a fumbling fuck in my room.

He was gone in the morning. I didn't remember much, only a few nice words. We chatted again, sneaked a drink during the leaving buffet, which we couldn't eat.

We had kept up an erotic correspondence, by work email and Skype sex on home laptops when everyone else was asleep.

He had arranged this meet, in Camden, where he lived.

I twiddled with my earrings. My shapely orange tanned legs drew glances, but only From the black guys outside the jacket shops, the Asian guys on the bag stalls, the Turkish guys at the food kiosks.

Trevor arrived at last.

He kissed me on both checks, which took me back a little.

He was casually dressed.

Blue Fred Perry shirt, khaki shorts and a pair of those mountain climber sandals everyone was wearing that summer.

He ordered a cappuccino and a pastel de nata.

He half-heartedly asked about work, my boyfriend.

He couldn't and didn't wait to talk about how great it was to live there.

All the personalities he knew, or had seen, at such and such club, or bar or bistro.

I noticed how he nervously kept rubbing his temples, and jerking his head around, and talking a little bit too loudly.

When I talked, he answered with quick yeses and nos.

He kept interrupting me and flicked his eyes all around the busy pavements.

I thought I'd grab the nervous baby bull by his not so big horns.

'Can we go back to your place?'

'Jesus, you are keen!'

I wanted to get away from this place, try to get somewhere where I felt more at ease.

'I've come a long way you know!'

Running in the sun

When that bell went we ran, we ran as fast as we could, ignoring the stitches in our sides, swinging our bags through the air...

Panting excitedly at the door.

'Mum! It's...the...holidays! No...more...school!'

The summer holidays had begun in 1960s Birmingham.

Our dads only had two weeks off from the factories so it was up to our mums to entertain us. We were about sixty miles from the sea so it was easy to get to, though Wales and nearby coast was freezing and we always wanted to go further south to warmer waters. But that cost money. So, Wales or Weston-super-Mare it was.

Wales was known for its terrible weather; wind that blew sand to scrub your face, and sometimes days of lashing rain.

I remember one morning on Shell Island; I dozed and rocked in a floating dreamy feeling. I woke and was rocking, as my blow-up bed floated on a foot of flood water.

So we preferred Weston. Though it was a poor first choice.

Weston was famous for the sea not being around much. You had to catch it. Be there at the right time. But most days all you saw was a vast expanse of dirty sand, the sea a dot on the horizon. Still we enjoyed playing in the mud, digging for shells or worms.

The deal was that the whole family went for two weeks then the fathers returned home. This was good for everyone. The fathers were free from kids and wives back home for five days until returning at the weekends. We don't know what they got up to, but we guessed it involved a lot of drinking. They looked worn out when they pitched up late Friday night.

The mums were left at the campsite with all the other mums and kids. We kids amused ourselves mainly; huge football games of thirty or more, exploring old war bunkers that smelled of piss and had ripped pieces of porn mags strewn about. We were a bit far from the beach, so we only went there once or twice a week. So we messed around in the camp pool, which never got hot and the amount of blooded heads on the kids testified to the care they had taken in building the concrete minefield surrounding the water.

The mums of course were happy; no men around. We kids came back to be fed usually with a stew and then went off again. Appearing now and then for cash for an ice lolly or some sweets. So, the women lay around, grabbing some rays and smoking and drinking a lot. They gathered in big packs on various sunbeds or camping seats and smoked and drank and bitched; but mostly we noticed they laughed. They didn't seem to do that much at home. And when I say laugh, I mean howls of laughter. We didn't know what they were laughing at and when we tried to sneak up and listen we were sent away with a swear word warning or a stick flung at your head.

Most summers went on like this, eight weeks camping, and we loved it because we were basically left to do what we wanted; we smoked and showed off our private parts to each other in the bunkers. We only saw our mums to be fed or for money, and then to go to bed, happy to go to sleep after an exhausting day. We lay on the camp beds and listened to the crickets and the gangs of women still laughing their heads off.

Our dads' visits involved a dads vs. kids game of footy or cricket, some swimming then off to the clubhouse at night, bingo and some jiving for the grown-ups, and crisps and pop for the kids sat in a long line on the wall outside swinging their legs happily.

But some summers we went on a family journey. This involved grandparents and uncles, aunts and cousins, all in a long caravan of second-hand cars towing trailers of camping gear. These I loved the best as we ventured into deepest Devon and farthest Cornwall. Interesting fishing villages with tiny lanes and gorgeous fish and chip suppers and tasty pasties.

We stayed on campsites for about two days then moved on. We stopped at places on the way. Hills to climb, views to be seen, ruins to be explored. We ventured into pastures unknown. I remember one time we had to go through field after field with signs warning of bulls and threats to close the gates. I was pushed out to open the gates and every car that passed me paid through the window for the favour and my valour.

The one year they decided to go on a big trip, through France to Spain. This was unheard of in those days. Working class people never went abroad; this was back before the mass package holidays and flights. I don't remember France much, we raced on through. But we arrived in Barcelona and when you look at the pictures and old cine films they took they looked like a group of bohemians. All dressed in their finery on the Ramblas...the working class of Brum, living the good life. One photo has my nan looking like Sophia Loren in pink sunglasses and a flowing flowery dress sat on a bench in Parc Guel; behind her my granddad stands proudly looking like Rudolph Valentino in his suit trousers and open necked shirt, greased back hair and pencil moustache. The campsite was not too far from the city. So we explored the lanes and avenues experiencing new smells and sounds; we felt like in a kids' adventure book.

And the sea! The sea was warm! And the sand was too hot for your feet, so we bought flip-flops and felt elegant. The food was weird. Rice with sea food, which we hesitantly picked at, at first, but grew to love, and meat on sticks from smoking grills, which we wolfed down. Our parents drank wine in the circle of chairs in the middle of the tents into the dark of night. I got ill, some bug or something. And I had a fever and felt like I was in a dream. I was carried into a hospital and remember this doctor with some metal thing on his head evilly grinning at me muttering in words like Tolkien's elves and his gold tooth sparkling in my dreary eyes as he bore down on me with a huge needle; then I floated off into a world of seas, ice creams and running...I saw myself running and laughing in the sun; never-ending running on the sand...until I woke.

The Anarchist

Tony was always an anarchist. From the top hat down to his winkle pickers; he never conformed. He always did things his way and usually this way was the way of trouble of one kind or another.

At school he had slapped a teacher who had hit him, so he got sent to borstal.

At borstal he hated the regimented rules and received beatings and lockdowns galore, he was never a violent, hard man; he took his beatings in his stride. He was always just never gonna toe the line, whatever they threw at him, he didn't care!

When punk happened his dad ran the Irish club and he worked behind the bar, we were all spiky hair and docs; he dressed as a nun or a jester. He walked round town like this, I mean we got some aggro for looking like punks in the late seventies but Tony got more than most, but as I said he took it all in his stride.

Tony never wanted to work, he took bar jobs but never considered it real work, he saw it as a cheap way to get pissed and he loved to get pissed.

He also loved to rob. If it could be stolen he would steal it, anything to make a quick quid.

When we lived in Brum we sold a load of the landlord's old furniture we found in the back sheds, he grassed us up and we got done for it.

We dealt a little speed and dope as well, and rented our flat out to the working girls and we went off to the pub with the money they gave us, and we got pissed most nights until we could go home.

When the New Romantics scene hit, Tony was already in the game, he hung around with the underground designers Kahn and Bell and contributed some of his creations to their cool store.

He featured in books and magazines; his was a face on the scene. It always made me laugh though cos underneath all the make-up and clobber I knew he was a bad 'un.

As I said Tony loved a bit of thievery. When the girls were working we robbed the punters' cars. If some stolen items came around we took the lot and flogged it to the shopkeepers on the Stratford Road. At one drunken party we were at we went downstairs to the chippy and he robbed a jar of pickled eggs off the counter, the cops were called and I got done for it. I never grassed on him, you just didn't do that.

Our life in Brum was exciting, prostitutes, drugs, clubs and bands. He was once offered the chance to join the cool posey group Fashion but after the audition he came back.

'Well?'

'Well. They offered me the job.'

'Great!'

'But, I turned them down.'

'For fuck's sake why?'

'I didn't like the singer's shoes.'

A few weeks later we watched them on *The Tube* in a Caribbean pub down the Ladypool Road.

'See; look at the state of them fucking shoes!'

You see it was all about the chaos for Tony.

He never read any books on anarchism; he just lived his life that way. Our lives were hard so he made the best out of it.

We once went to a posh hotel in Brum and pretended to be Siouxsie and the Banshees and he blagged us in to a plush suite, and we ordered champagne and roast beef sandwiches from room service. We left in the morning and no one was any the wiser.

He eventually outgrew Brum and moved to London, I went travelling instead.

Once in London he hit the underground squatting scene. Everyone squatted in those days: punks, would-be rock musicians, fashion designers; it wasn't all just druggies and drunkards. Young people couldn't get flats like in Brum, so a whole sub-culture of squatting developed. If you wanted to meet musicians you met through a squat. These squats often held parties and they were righteous affairs.

I visited him in-between my journeys and stayed for a few weeks or so to collect enough dole money to be off again. The squats were filled with characters. In Tony's there were some girls from a fashion designers college who ran little stalls around Camden Lock, not the multi-marketed mega stalls etc. of today. Tony made T-shirts and I sold them with him outside the Blue Elephant pub. When we sold a T-shirt we went in for a beer. He sold more of his clothes on the stalls and his stuff was much in demand; he didn't make much money from it but enough to supplement his dole money. The guy who had broke into the Queen's bedroom, Michael Fagan, slept in the squat too with his two kids when they weren't with their mum in an Indian tepee village in Wales. Tony booked a club and got a Queen look-alike to sit in a bed with Mr Fagan sitting next to her singing along to 'God Save the Queen' by the Pistols on a backing track.

But the most important person who lived there was Claudia. A real femme fatale. Short cropped bleached bob and a bohemian mix of clothes and a heroin habit brought over from the US. She was so infamous that the Damned had a song about her. Everyone fell for her, including me. But in Tony she had found a soulmate, sex never came into it, even though Tony was bi. They partied and drugged every day, going to this gathering, this rehearsal session. They hob-knobbed with famous musos and artists and infamous characters in the squatting scene. They got onto every guest list. Everyone wanted to know them, to be around them...this sexual bombshell of trouble and this weirdly-dressed over the top character.

Artists invited them to their openings. I don't know what it was but they drew the famous and would-be famous artists and musos to them. And she got him into smack. The last I saw of him, as I went off to travel for about ten years, his habit wasn't bad, it was just a cool little thing to do, and it went with their personas, their image if you like.

It ended up being twenty-five years before we saw each other again, we met in Camden of course and I brought my son with me. The old Camden was gone now but a lot of the old faces still remained, others had passed on, either to fame and fortune or to the grave.

He was shaky when I met him, and his face drawn. I knew he needed a little fix but he tried to hide it, so he drank a lot. We sat opposite the lock with a pint and caught up.

He was now a kept man; a Greek love affair between him and an old artist and friend and muse of Lucian Freud. They had a farmhouse in Wales and a villa in France and a grotty little flat in Camden. His lover hadn't come.

'He doesn't like people much.'

We reminisced. He told me he had done proper bird for burglary. Over a year.

'How was it?'

'Ah, you know, if you can avoid the violence it's just boredom that's the killer but there was plenty of horse to ride it out on.'

'And Claudia?'

'Claudia, that fucking bitch, she fucked my life up, got me this little habit I can't shake off my back. She went back to the States, married a musician and then an armed robber, and then I lost contact. Hope she's fucking dead!'

He wanted to take me round some of the super cool fashion stalls under the viaduct. Where he was welcomed by the proprietors and they showed me his designs. His work was still very sort after and I could see he was proud of that. And I was proud of him. He promised to come to Prague and stay but I knew he wouldn't. But the next day he rang me at a mate's house and said...

'I'll be over on Tuesday, can you get smack over there?' I knew he was on one.

'Listen, Tone, I don't want no fucking smack shit going on if you visit, my missus wouldn't put up with it, but you are welcome to come please!'

'Yeah I understand.' And he put the phone down.

I haven't heard from him since, and he took his profile off Facebook. I wanted to get him to visit, I wanted to apologise for having a go at him about the smack, I wanted, I wanted...I don't know what. I wanted to cuddle him and help him, and try and have a go at reliving the old days, but with me off the booze and him on the smack we just couldn't have a relationship anymore.

And this makes me sad.

Vessel in Vain

I looked up from my paper, found the barman and ordered another cognac and beer. I was sat in the tap bar of the Coach and Horses, an old Birmingham pub, not changed much since the seventies, which was good. It was quiet, no TV, no music; just perfect for a late morning drink.

I had come from my meeting with the psychologist; I had problems with drinking and depression.

I took out my electronic ciggie and held it up to the barman, and he nodded, so I puffed away. I thought about what the psycho had said. That I was responsible for everything I had done, good or bad. Everything I had said, everything I had seen. And I looked around the boozer which was like so many others I had got pissed in before and thought – no, I'm not!

It just came to me like that. I wasn't responsible. It wasn't my fault, any of it. All I am is an out of control tug drifting on the ocean, and what waves life sent me on had nothing to do with me.

I liked this idea. It wasn't my fault! Any of it. I take no responsibility whatsoever! It was just the sea of life that I rode on with no control.

And I started to picture people sitting in front of my table.

The guy I had punched at Coventry for his scarf. The guy whose nose I had broken in a bar in Lisbon. The guy we had beaten and robbed at school for his dinner money. These figures sat and I waved them away. Next were a line of women. Some I had cheated on, some I had conned into sex with empty promises and bullshit chat-up lines. The simple but beautiful girl I had pretended to be a model agent to, who I got to strip for me in a bar I was looking after when it was closed. The dwarf I fucked just to say I had fucked a dwarf. The line was long and one by one they came to the table and I waved them away. The guy whose house we had robbed. The landlord whose furniture we had loaded up on a lorry and fucked off with. The owners of the Irish club whose safe we had robbed. They kept coming. And mostly more women. The ones I had swindled my way into their beds and then hounded them to do something they didn't really didn't wanna do. And lastly, the hot dog salesman from outside a gig in Leicester where I had ordered twenty dogs for everyone and then ran off.

I wasn't safe but I felt no fear. Images came and I dismissed them. It wasn't my fault! Don't you see?

It was life that did it, the turbulent waters of life that tossed these people my way and what I did or said wasn't my fault...that's just how it is, I sat and smiled and supped my beer and sank the brandy.

'Another cognac, my good friend!'

'You seem to be in a good mood?'

'I have discovered the secret to life.'

'No, shit, and that is?'

'You see it doesn't matter what you do or say, we are but empty vessels floating on the sea of life and whatever has happened none of it is your fault, that's just the way it goes!'

'So, you are saying that every bad thing you have done, every shit thing you have done to someone is not your fault; you are not to blame?'

'Precisely! I am not guilty of anything. None of it was my fault. I take no blame for all my mistakes and bad deeds. No blame for the people I have fucked over and done wrong.'

'You don't think you have to take some of the responsibility for your actions?'

'That's just it you see, I take no responsibility at all, none of it was my fault. Life is to blame not me!'

'So, with that logic I can basically do anything I want and not feel guilty about it?'

'Sure!'

He took the glass from my hand and punched me right in the face.

'Not my fault!'

I finished my drink and dabbed the blood from my nose, put the paper under my arm and walked out.

Trotsky in the Amazon

We had never been religious in our family, well there was one uncle and aunt who we hated visiting as they always dragged us along to Sunday School meetings. But I didn't mind that in the end as I got off with Julie Clarke, the best looking girl; and she wasn't religious at all as I found out in the cemetery after class.

In school one of the best lessons we had was Religious Education. And that was saying something as it was a crappy school; full of corporal punishment and depressed teachers, so mostly we just fucked around or fucked off to a mate's house to wait out the day.

But for a change, in RE we had a cool guy who taught us about ethics and about different religions; and when he started the sex class by writing 'fucking, prick and cunt' on the board we knew this was something to pay attention to.

He took us on trips to all the local religious centres around our way; mosques, synagogues, Hindu temples and even a Quaker meeting house. So, we learnt firsthand about these religions and how they did things. It didn't make me want to be involved in any religion but it was interesting to know about them.

My mates who went to the Catholic school had a different experience. They had Catholic doctrine beaten into them by nuns and priests. And there was always stories around about fiddlers. So, we got off lightly I think. The Church of England was always a bit of a wimpy religion. All afternoon tea and crumpets and summer jamborees. Pretty harmless really.

When punk came around I was introduced to anarchism; with its ideas on atheism and its agnostic stand-point. And I wrote anti-religious lyrics for our songs. So, after that I was pretty anti-religion and loved getting into arguments. We used to go to the students union in Manchester where there was always some God-botherer spouting fire and brimstone outside the union building.

We wound them up by first arguing about the Bible and then by saying stuff like 'The Romans had the right idea, throw you to the lions!' and 'If he comes back we will nail him up again!' They got pretty red-faced about that one.

Then in 1990 I went to Brazil, I had become disillusioned with the politics I had been involved with for the last ten years or so, so fancied a change. I supposedly went to teach English but I mostly lived a hedonistic existence of booze, drugs, and parties.

But two things affected me, both to do with religion.

One day I was walking down the street in Belem, a city on the Amazon, and saw a big crowd of people piling into a hall. I sauntered over and paid my ten cruzero entrance fee. Inside I saw on stage a madman ranting and raving about Christ. He was American but shouted at the audience in perfect Portuguese, and around the walls stood other Americans looking like CIA agents; they were there to keep the peace. In front of this man was an audience of poor locals hanging onto his every word, and the gist of it was this: 'You are all bad sinners, and you will all go to hell if you don't give us your money!' And unbelievably the people gave what little they had to these fraudsters. I tried to argue with some, telling them not to do it, but got lifted up by the CIA and thrown out the door.

The second religious encounter couldn't have been more different.

I was teaching a class of some teacher who was sick. After the class this skinny dark skinned young man came up to me. 'I found what you said about our country interesting.' I had been political, talking of the poor and how much I hated the president and that, and he said, 'But, do you know the real Brazil?'

'I think so; I've been to enough seedy bars in dodgy areas, so I think I know it pretty well.'

'Do you want to see the real Brazil?'

'Sure.'

So he gave me an address to go to where there was some gathering and then he promised me a trip or some such thing after.

I bounced up to the address on a late Saturday lunchtime to find that it was a Catholic seminary! After umming and ahhing outside for a bit, I smoked a fag then decided it would be a good experience to see what happens in these places, so rang the bell. Inside there was a party going on, loads of young people were dancing Lambada, the girls' knickers visible as they twirled. And older, I found out later, teachers, writers and other intellectuals, stood around yapping away whilst swigging back the Caipirinha.

I was introduced to other young trainee priests and got stuck into the booze. They showed me around and in their simple rooms I saw their books; the Bible of course, but also, Marx and Gramsci, and even Trotsky...I mean Trotsky in the Amazon! Then the music was turned off and people started to give speeches. I understood the gist and Joao my student translated the rest. One after the other the intellectuals and the trainees gave anti government rants. Slagging off the authorities and arguing for action to help the poor and working classes. I was amazed... it was like being back home in a union meeting or a miners' strike rally. They pointed the mic at me and in my broken Portuguese I said I loved Brazil and the people but hated the president. They cheered and slapped my back and poured me another drink.

But I wondered if this talk was all show by the church, just to gain favour with the poor as the evangelists had with their wrath at the unfaithful method.

After an hour or so they said, 'You ready to see the real Brazil now?' Shit, I thought this was it!

'Sure lead on!'

We got a lift in an old Ford and pulled up outside a make-shift bar; corrugated iron walls and roof and various old tables and chairs and a freezer and football photos behind a wooden table kind of thing nailed onto two oil drums. We were near the edge of a Favela near to the river.

The place looked and felt dangerous and all talk stopped when we drew up. But as soon as the shirtless drinkers saw the two trainee priests their spirits and friendliness rose. Backs were slapped, hands were shaken, and cold Antarctica beers were pulled from the freezer and plonked down in front of us on a hastily wiped Formica table. I was introduced and everyone shook my hand, from the druggy looking teenager to the pot-bellied guys in Bermudas. Even the dodgiest looking guys with moustaches who looked like guns for hire ventured over and shook my hand.

I could see these guys were respected and wondered why.

After a few beers we bid our farewells and were told to come back later for a farewell one. We ventured into the labyrinth of the Favela. Because of the river all the buildings were on stilts, built high in case of flooding. The two guys were welcomed at every turn. Some old women kissing their hands. We were welcomed into homes that had little in the way of furniture or anything else for that matter but were given cakes or bread and of course drink; beer or moonshine. The families and the guys chatted and I was questioned about the UK and what the hell was I doing here in Brazil? They really couldn't understand why I would come here from Europe, I tried to tell them about the poverty and the fights of working people in Europe but they dismissed my stories with a wave of their hands.

We were shown a big wooden building and this I found out was a community workshop, where the locals made excellent furniture that was sold collectively. This had been set up by the trainee priests. The people showed me other projects with pride. Organic toilet blocks that had replaced the shed at the end of the plank from your hut where you shat from a great height into the street. The trainees had introduced compost toilets at ground level and this was helping to keep the place hygienic. I was impressed. I was introduced to a very dangerous looking man, with a four inch scar down his face and a pistol in his waist. He told me that the trainees were welcome here, the police never came and if I hadn't been with them I would have been stripped and running naked trying to escape by now. I grinned and said, 'Well, thanks for that, I suppose.' We said our goodbyes and had a last farewell drink in the bar and left.

This was no religion as such, no preaching or asking for cash. The guys' role they felt as priests was to fight for the poor. And that was why they were so respected by the people and hated by the hierarchy of the church. I found out more about these Marxist priests and found they had a long history in South America. They had been persecuted and hunted and often thrown out of the church, a few had been murdered.

I left Brazil but kept up a correspondence with Joao. He sent me a picture of a reed hut where he now lived after graduating. He was in the forest helping the Indians fight against the ranchers burning down the forest.

After two years I got no more correspondence.

The Factories

My mum got me the job when I was fifteen and a half; she worked in the office porta cabin outside the factory. The factory was a knocked together shed of corrugated iron, with holes everywhere and fucking freezing all the time. We had to keep the doors open because of the fumes from the bitumen and the dust from the jute. In the corner was a little hut with a fire and a kettle and nuddy pictures pinned to the wall. We huddled in there in break times. The lads were friendly from the off despite my spiky black hair. They were a mixture of troublemakers and ex-cons, a few were Elvis fans. Despite the papers running stories of offs between Teds and punks they didn't give a shit. Addo Blout, Teddy boy and fighter. Bunsy Owen, fighter and crook. There were a few non teds and non crooks just guys from the poor estates; Mickey Wills, constantly having the piss taken out of him cos of his long greasy hair. One of the gangers was a pretty straight guy, from the kind of posh area. But mainly the boss believed in giving ex-cons a second chance. And they were always pleasant to my mum who looked after them and sorted out stuff for them as some couldn't write. One of the most violent guys was Neil Stubbs; been in prison for assaulting his girlfriend with a hammer, he said, 'People will learn not to mess me around. He had been picked on as he attended the Catholic school but lived on the mostly Protestant estate and walked past Harry Cheshire school every afternoon and soon learned to fight well and people left him alone. He would catch the rats running round the factory and play cricket with them; the kind of guy who when his brother was taking a bath would come in and take a shit in the bath. But he was never violent unless provoked. He was a fun guy to have around. But the biggest joker was Tom Carey. One day I arrived to an empty factory and the machines silent. Addo caught me outside. 'Don't go in, he has a knife and has threatened everyone and has them sitting in the mechanic pit, shitting themselves. They think he has gone mad, so don't go in.' He hadn't gone mad he was just fucking around. The machines made felt paper, for waterproofing roofs. You put jute in one end, and sometimes had to prod it with a broom to get it through; these days the whole place would be closed cos of health and safety. It then went through rolling line; a garnet which constantly broke, and the boss loved to tinker with, then though rollers high and low, and then through bitumen, and finally through sand and gathered onto the rollers in 25 metre tubes. Our job was basically to keep the rolls moving, making sure they didn't break; we needed full 25-metre rolls at the end. But the line broke all the time and we could hardly work our fingers they were that cold. We all had layers and layers of clothes on and spots all over our bodies from the jute.

One day the health guy came round to inspect and ask questions. The boss and my mum weren't there so Tom pretended to be the boss. 'And does any jute or bitumen get into the canal at all?'

'Oh yeah, we often throw bad bales of jute in there and empty old used bitumen in there.' The health and safety guy was in heaven busy writing it all down. Tom got a written warning for that.

Eventually we moved to a new industrial estate with a huge new factory. The machines fitted into one side of the place and there was room for stacker trucks to shift bales of jute and pallets of felt paper. On the other side were the offices and our break room. It was modern and huge, so huge we could have races in the stacker trucks at night when the management weren't there. We had three shifts; 6 till 2pm, 2 till 10pm and the night shift 10 till 6am. The morning shift was tough what with having to get up so early on a freezing morning. But on Friday we got paid at 2 and went straight to the pub nearby. The nightshift was second best; the first two days were hard, you felt zombied out till your body clock got used to it, this was also good for a Friday; you went home at 6 got a few hours' kip then joined the morning shift for beer at 2pm. The afternoon shift was the worst; you just managed to grab a pint in the week and had to work Friday evenings, we got round this by starting to work on a Sunday, so we also picked up our wages at 2pm and hit the pub with the other gangs. The nightshift was also good as there were no managers around, so we fucked around a lot; stacker truck racing, rat cricket and when really bored we let the machine catch fire and stood smoking outside while the fire brigade put the fire out. I always asked for jute duty, that way I could load up the machine and then have half an hour to sit amongst the bales and write punk lyrics for my band. One night the guys from the pub came back with Graham a reformed criminal now a ganger and we proceeded to have a game of football putting all the windows out in the offices, Graham got sacked and we all got written warnings. Like I said before the boss believed in giving people another chance so after three months Graham got re-employed. I had the chance to go and work in a hotel and train to be a chef, so left. The job was a terrible job to be honest but the crack with the lads was one of the best I've ever had on a job. A few years later I visited the new factory; out of town and super high tec. The guys just pushed buttons. I could see they missed the mucking in and around but all were now making good money. So they were happy I guess but I think they all missed the old corrugated factory where they had all started, for the ramshackle work and the fucking around and for that little hut where we huddled for warmth and told tall tales.

Rockabilly and Custard

-He's sacked cos he fucking smells!

-Smells? What do mean sacked cos he smells? Who smells?

-Get your gear and get the fuck out of here.

Whoosh!

The tub of crème brûlée custard flew across the kitchen, all watched it, as if in slow motion, turning, turning...

Splosh!

Knives came from Levi jean pockets and in unison:

Flick!

***

-Sommage!

-One mussel starter one pate, one Diane, one chasseur.

-Table 5 Via!

-Where the fuck are the salads for 4?

-Chef, we've run out of fresh tomatoes?

-Run out of fucking tomatoes, for fuck's sake! You fuck-head, go climb up those pig bins and fetch us some out, you dig?

My hangover was really kicking in now. You dig! I poured some masala and knocked it down, retched and waited for things to become visible through the tears.

-You, go and get me a beer from the bar, pronto.

-Chef, I'm busy.

-And you'll be even busier if you don't go and get me a fucking beer now.

***

-She's in, chef.

-Shit where?

I took off my cap ran my fingers threw my now floppy greasy, once magnificent, quiff and peered through the hatch into the little bistro annex.

-Classy Chassis.

-You think? Not pissed off at all?

-Na, she looks fine, man, real fine.

-Yeah, thanks for telling me.

-You, knob-head, go take a whiskey and dry to the lady on table eight.

-What about the money, chef?

-Tell 'em to put it on my tab.

-Shiite!

-Yeah, and while we're at it bring one for me too.

I watched the leggy brunette take off her leather coat to reveal a pink cardigan and a grey full skirt under which were seamed stockings. She bobbed her curly locks as the maître d' pushed her chair in. She took out a gold leaf and pouted her blue lips to light it. She received the whiskey, smiled and shot it back in one.

Alena is her name and boy does A-l-e-n-a spell trouble. No doubt about it, this was bound to end badly. I should never have started, but an offer this good seldom comes around.

***

She lit up the hotel Marais basement bar like a cluster bomb.

That den of sad fuckers. That bar of late night wasters waiting for the morning trains to beds.

The poncy waiters in a corner, the managers at the bar, the rockabillies and kitchen porters round a pool table, next to the jukebox. Sharing over-flowing tables with pimps, pushers and working girls.

Snorting, sniffing, necking, and stabbing. The night's stresses and stains wiped away with powder and puffs; shootin' and a tooting.

We are all wired, all in need of an unwind. All in need of an adrenaline cool down. So, we soaked it in brine and brought it back up with rolled notes.

I had seen her before, obviously, how could you miss her? But somehow this time, I managed to get my mashed up head together long enough, or maybe because it was mashed, to make a move.

-Can I bum one of those?

She smiles.

-Sure.

-Original.

-Sorry?

-Asking for a cigarette, usually I have only to put one to my lips and I get an avalanche of lighters in my face.

-I've lost my lighter. And my fags and wallet too to be honest.

-Can I get you a drink too then?

-Sure, half a lager and a brandy.

-Sounds good. Two halves of Stella and two Martans.

-Cheers.

A waiter went to the jukebox and put some kind of dance music on...

The place hushed, a huge tattooed sous chef stood, walked over, slapped the guy, kicked the jukey, re-selected, and...Gene Vincent...'Baby Blue'.

-Nice.

-You're the chef at Les Negress verte.

-You know me?

-I know your food.

-And?

-You know it's good, do you have to ask?

-I need to hear it said sometimes.

-Well. It's very good, though...

-Though's not good, no one says though an...

-Chill, darling. You're wired, love another Martan?

I necked it.

-So, though?

-I was just going to say that your Bouillabaisse is lacking a certain something, that's all.

-You think?

-There's a sweet little fish found in the North, that I always feel is the key, and a stock that's been bubbling for years.

-Oh the sweet fish of the North, not an easy catch, and an old stock pot is difficult to find these days too.

-Pity, but I recognize and appreciate your inclusion of saffron and truffle.

-You have a very delicate palate, madam.

-Why thank you kind, sir.

-Cheers.

-Are you here alone?

-Well, kind of, but I'm my own woman.

-I'm sure you are, but.

-Well, I came in with Stoney but as usual he seems to have disappeared.

I looked at her. She had said his name with no interest, no fear.

I tried to show nonchalance.

-Yeah Stoney, the erm, businessman.

-You mean gangster.

-Well, I...

-It's OK, that's what he is, you don't have to be scared.

-I'm not, just curious that's all.

-Curious I like, and don't worry I was left alone hours ago I don't expect him to be back, happens a lot. Fancy a line?

-Delighted.

Just one I told myself. Just one, be nice then get the hell out of there, but she was gorgeous.

***

-You fucked who?

My mate Tony was always one to fly of the handle at the slightest.

-You know, the femme fatale, from the bar, Baby Blue.

-Baby fucking Blue? Are you living in an Eddie Cochran movie or what? Do you know who she is?

-Sure. And it's Gene Vincent actually.

-And you're not worried?

-Should I be?

-You bet your fucking sweet arse you should be.

-I know she is involved with some dodgy geezer and that but...

-Some dodgy geezer? Are you for fucking real? She is married to...

-Married? Shit, well there you go.

-There you fucking go? Listen, my friend, I don't think you have grasped the seriousness of what I am saying to you.

-F-Fuck man, I've fucked married women before.

-Yeah, and that always turned out well didn't it. And besides you've never fucked a wife of a fucking total psycho before.

-So bit of a badass then?

-Bit of a bad ass? Are you kidding me? Billy Hill?

-Psycho Billy.

-You're a fucking dick, you know that. Billy fucking Hill, *the* Billy fucking Hill!

-It doesn't matter how often you say it, I've never heard of the cunt.

-This guy is an enforcer, he tortures for the big boys, he does it and loves it, they say. And you fucked his missus, Jesus H Christ. You'd better scram the hell out of here, daddy O.

-You worry too much. She's been hanging round with some other grody clyde by the way.

-Who?

-Stoney.

-Fuck, man, I don't think I even should be talking to you anymore.

-Don't you see, man? If she is supposed to be with this Hill cat, and she is doing the rounds with this other odd ball, then...maybe.

-Oh I see, maybe you can play them off against each other is that it? You gotta be kidding me, you are real gone kid, is she worth it?

-My man, she's a screamer!

-A screamer's a hot car, man, not a chick.

-Whatever.

***

I carried on seeing her. We met in little Italian milk bars in the day, and the press club at night round the corner of the casino district, full of gay croupiers and grey-faced whiskey journalists. But our place, our favourite place was the Hope bar, near the meat markets. Opened at 3am closed at noon. We squeezed in-between porter drinking barrow boys and brandy drinking meat men, with blood on their hands and chops in bags swapped for fivers at the bar. We snorted in the men's cubicles and fucked in the ladies, and took it all in, the whole scene, the fifties tunes, the fifties suits of dodgy geezers with vans and greyhounds on leads. We would go back to my gaff for more snorts and sniffs and muff diving for multiples and blowjobs with chili.

***

-Well, what we have here is a Mexican standoff, gentlemen.

A couple of errand boys were stood in the middle of quiffed chefs with their knives drawn and their caps off.

-I told you this fucking punk is sacked cos he smells.

-So, what if he smells, he lives in a shit hole gets little sleep and works his bollocks off.

-But he fucking smells, and it ain't good for business.

-He's a fucking KP, no one sees him, who complained?

-Some of the staff.

-The fucking waiting staff you mean.

-If he goes we all go.

-You don't wanna start this shit, I am telling you. When my boss hears about this knife shit, man.

-Tell your boss he ain't going nowhere.

-And I'm telling you he's fucking sacked.

-In that case, you tell your fucking boss, we are on strike, from tomorrow no one works until he gets his fucking job back.

-I'll tell him.

They could do no more, just two of them. With eight chefs armed with knives and ten KPs armed with pots and custard.

They walked calmly through the group, and sniffed a look up and down at a few whilst flicking custard off their pin-stripes and winkle pickers.

-We'll be in touch.

Hobo Code

I lost it all, the mortgage, the wife, the home. I have the clothes on my back and what is in my knapsack, and my guitar. And I took to the rails and the highways. I have grown to love the road, the freedom; the joy of watching the stars at night, I sleep better now, like a log. When I had things and responsibility I never slept well. We have a code us roaming men. On the gate or fence are etched symbols to give other men an indication of what lies inside. Old Henry taught me the symbols; an old man about eighty I met at a hobo campsite and spent some nights eating and drinking and chatting with. He had been homeless in the eighties when unemployment was high; he took to the road and never went back.

'We copied the symbols from the American hobos, and now we leave symbols outside a house, on a wall, a gate, with a stone or a knife. We tell which way to head, where to stop and where to avoid. There's one for where they *Enjoy a song*. You know, after I have chopped wood and had a meal...'

'Will you give us a tune on the guitar.' 'And I give 'um a rendition of 'Vessel in Vain' or 'Hang Down your Head;' accompanied by my battered Martin.'

There's other symbols to look out for.

-Here she makes a great pie is a good one. Often savoury beef and onion and sometimes in summer blueberry or raspberry. 'Have another slice, please,' is music to my ears.

One to avoid if possible is *Man likes to talk politics*. And he is usually a farmer with right wing views, and even though he gave you work he still can't help himself talking about lazy men. 'The man today is basically a lazy animal. Doesn't want to work, always looking for a handout, not you I may add, you worked hard that's for sure.'

We were near this place near Coventry, the guy had asked us to trim his lawn and cos he wasn't feeling well went off to bed. At the end of the day when we went to find him he was nowhere to be seen.

Then we found him; brown bread in bed. We had heard that this guy was a recluse and had money stashed around and he was always good to us; offering fruitcake and tea as well as cash for odd jobs. But his house didn't look up to much. Papers piled high in the corridors like the plates in the sink. We looked for the money but felt bad about it.

There was a bowl of change on the TV and we couldn't even bring ourselves to touch that. As we left we passed a stand of old umbrellas and decided that he wouldn't mind us borrowing a couple as it was a stormy night; so we left him with his hidden stash and thanked him for the brollies.

There are other parts of the code; unwritten but mostly strictly followed.

When hitching a lift you always ask the guy there before you where he wants you to stand.

When entering a camp a place near the fire is always offered and whatever you have is shared around. If you have a bag of backy you offer it around for everyone to have a roll up, that way you get offered tea or soup from a tin warmed on the embers.

I've been on the road for two years now and I have had a good time all in all. I've met some great guys and girls, and some kind folks. Don't get me wrong it isn't all sweetness in the moonlight. I've been beaten up for no reason and sexually assaulted more than once. And sent off from a door with a hurl of abuse and often a boot to follow.

We try not to steal, but sometimes a farmer's field ain't gonna miss an apple or two, but not big stuff, not from houses, that's part of the code; it would affect others' chances so we don't do it. Don't get me wrong there are guys who will steal your shoes while you're walking, but they are usually young and addicted to drugs, so I see why they need to do it.

But one time a chance came that was too good to pass up.

Me and this old guy Henry were doing some general labour work around a big house, you know one with a garage full of motors and a few servants and a gardener.

This guy was a miserable sod who didn't like us much but never passed up the chance of getting cheap labour. He took us to this boat house down by the river.

'See those boxes stacked there? Well, most of it is crap so just go through it quickly and throw most of it out unless you think something might be worth a bit or be important.'

Most of it was real tat; old papers and bits of old ornaments. We put it all into two piles; worth a look at, and garbage. I was reaching for a big box on a top shelf when this little envelope fell out; it had a red seal on it. I opened it.

If you are reading this you are near, one more clue to go then it will be yours.

It was very old and obviously had been hiding away for a long time.

I read on. *Take the road out of town until you see two dangly trees. Wait for sundown and the shadow of the two trees will cross. Dig here.*

I showed it to Henry and we decided to follow the instructions, it wasn't obviously that important to the grumpy little rich guy.

We finished our chores and got paid; no pic was offered which encouraged us even more to follow the law of the letter.

We stomped off with our packs on our backs, we took the road out of the town and walked for about forty-five minutes then we spotted the two dangly tress, in a field with nothing else around. We sat just a way from them and waited for the sun to come down. We didn't build a fire but shared fags and some fruit, and waited. The sun came down and the shadows crossed. The shadows met about forty feet away from the trees.

We walked there; we each had a trowel, a useful tool for many things and which hobos always carry for when they need to bury their crap, another hobo code.

'This looks like the place, what do you think?'

'Seems about right, shall we dig?'

'Why not we ain't stealing anything, guy didn't even know the letter was there, and he don't seem to need much more of anything.'

We dug and about two feet down we hit metal. It turned out to be a tin box, not too big. We opened it.

Inside was another letter and something else.

Well done, you have followed the clues and found something of what this family had stolen to make their fortune, so now you have the chance to get one back over them for me.

It was a beautiful piece and we passed it to each other and inspected it.

'What do you think? We ain't no thieves but the person who planned this seemed to want whoever found it to keep it.'

'Let's take it with us into the next county and see about selling it.'

'Fifty, fifty?'

'Fifty, fifty!'

Mr Albion

It's late, it's raining, it's Tuesday night. The Queen's Head stands alone amongst derelict land and boarded up rows of houses. A little light standing out in the rusty coloured sky. An old Union Jack flaps, tattered on a pole hanging from above the creaking sign.

Thought I'd pop in to one of my old haunts. Was my local for years. We lived in the next street. They've mostly gone now; the streets.

I take my half glass to the bar.

'Do you have any mild, you know old style mild.'

'We have draught dog bolter bitter and Ape ale.'

Jesus H Christ!

'Just half a lager then.'

'Would you like Czech or wheat?'

'Just the old kind!'

The guy with a beard and a hair bun smirks and pulls me a Staropramen.

'Two quid to you, mate.'

'Two quid for half a lager!'

'Welcome to modern Britain, old man!'

I take my half and sit on a chrome backed red leather seat.

I looked around; no telly to watch the footy on, just some repetitive music blaring away. Difficult to even chat in here!

There are groups of well-dressed students knocking back shots and laughing too loudly.

'Last orders, gents and ladies!'

It's only ten thirty! I thought we had all night drinking these days.

I sink me half, put on my battered trilby and my tatty mac over my thread-worn stripped suit, and tie; pull up my collar...'Good evening.' And push out into the thick drizzle.

I stand at the bus stop; the bus is late as they always are these days. It takes eight stops till I get to my neighbourhood. There is a little more life here, though I don't know anyone anymore.

But it all makes me angry and nostalgic. An Asian shop, open all hours. One time they shopped for us now they have taken over the shops that closed at five-thirty and half day on Wednesdays. Now they can take our money anytime of the day.

I kick the kerb with my ancient scuffed brogues; once they had always shone.

A Greek kebab shop stands where Alf's fish and chips once stood. I look at the menu; no fish and chips...I spit on the pavement and light up a Woodbine.

My health's not what it was. Doc says I'll croak it if I don't stop the fags but, he don't care really.

And I let it be this way; it was my fault.

I remember when the trains ran on time (but I had supported privatisation).

I remember kids in the street playing safely, kicking a ball; now their grannies get kicked in the head for their pensions. The once proud working man controlled these streets along with the rolling pins of the mothers with crying babies wrapped round their middle. I had wanted the unions destroyed, the young sent for national service; wanted a throw-back to the glory days, when our unfurled flag smothered everything.

Now the road seems filled with round-shouldered men staggering past boarded up shops struggling to get home or to a bedsit to sit alone with another can and some reality programme about people on benefits. I pass an alley and sees kids, twelve, thirteen dealing; they look up at me with red skunk eyes, give a toothless grin and carry on.

-What the fuck you want, old man?

I walk away slowly and hum to myself... 'There always be an England'...Got a bloody tear in me eye, saft sod!

I get back to me two up two down. Roll up pages of the *The Daily Mail* and get a coal fire going. I get the coal from a garden centre these days; a product of bloody Poland. I had believed the promises of Thatcher about not closing the pits. I should have listened to Scargill, I know now don't I? I read the front page of a *Sun*; *'Read the messages of the missing girl!' Jesus, who wants to read that? That's not fucking news!* I throw it onto the fire.

On the telly, the prime minister is denying that he lied to the nation again, fucking idiot he is! Sold us a promise of being free, out of Europe, now we have no workers to pick fruit or load baggage at airports and every one on short-term contracts; wages so low they need benefits too and food banks; breaks my heart, but I fell for it didn't I. It's my fault! I voted for these Etonians. Why did I believe they would help the working man? When I look back now I see it was them! It was them that did all this! They promised me a Great Britain and I got a shite Britain. I am sorry! Sorry for the families struggling, the kids with only gangs and drugs to look forward to.

I change channels. On the other side a programme about the most successful criminal gangs of Northern England, then a film about D-Day. I watch with a lump in me throat. And begin to cry again. This happens a lot these days; maybe loneliness? The doctor gives me some pills for me nerves, they help a bit. I turn it off and pour a scotch from a half bottle, one of my few treats these days. I pull back the curtains. In the house opposite an argument is going on, I can feel the fists coming. I look out down the road at the rusting statue of the steelworks standing as a memorial, where I worked till they shut it down. Not profitable any more they said. And I look further down to the now silent docks, nothing going in or out these days. I take off my suit and clothes and get under me tatty old patchwork quilt, Gladys had handsewn. I turn the lamp off; take a last look through the gap in the curtains at the horizontal rain battering the window and close my eyes.

Born a Rocker, Die a Rocker

Lee was a rock and roller even at twelve years old. Our school played his school at footy and there was this guy; lanky body and flowing locks, socks rolled down and he was doing flicks and step overs and nutmegs long before Ronaldo was born. We were plodders and hoofers and were told by our coach to nobble the flashy little fucker on the wing. We tried but couldn't get near him and he took the flying tackles and punches in his stride. We lost three nil; he scored all three goals.

Later we went to the same high school and played on the same team and we became friends.

A lot of people didn't like him because he was flash, except the girls of course, but I liked his panache, I was a bit that way myself so we hit it off. I remember going on bike trips a lot and playing football, of course, and scrumping apples from farmers or a little stealing from the paper shop where we worked delivering newspapers in the mornings before school.

One summer we were allowed to go camping alone for the first time, we were about thirteen. Me and Lee and the Roberts brothers went to a campsite near Evesham; a riverside holiday town not far from Brum. The Roberts were expert thieves and we hit the small town for knives, and a record shop that sold some punk singles and on our best day Nigel Roberts walked out of store with a whole fucking bike! Like I said...top thieves.

Punk had arrived and me and Lee grabbed it with relish. Here was something new, something different. We had both never quite fitted in with the soul crowd, the pub and factory brigade...we wanted out! So it came at just the right time for us. We had our own little punk club, the Irish club, and lee was the singer of course in one of the first bands we all formed at fourteen. And up there on that stage he took all the flash from the footy and posed around and let it rip; for me a perfect front man.

Punk was all about doing things different, we were offered no chances to be someone or something from school or parents. There was no university waiting for us, just a factory, a wife and kids and beer and footy or the dole. We wanted more and punk gave us the chance to aim higher; to look for other things to become. Looking back at that little den of thieves and strays and outsiders, you can see what came out of the punk DIY ethos. Some became politicians, some fashion designers some professors of sociology, some writers and it was all thanks to punk. And Lee became a rocker, for life!

His story is a mixed one, one of failures, downs and almost theres. But it is a story of a kid from the streets of Kiddy who sang his way around the world, and for me, had a lot of success. But it is one also littered with almost made it big moments. And he is quite famous, a well known rock and roller in the niche circles of rock, and he touched the stars but never quite managed to hang on. But the question is was he a success? Depends on how you measure success really. Let us look back and try and piece this thing together.

The stories are many so I'll summarise for you.

His second band were more post-punk and did well headlining with Pop Will Eat Itself and the Wonderstuff who later signed for Chapter 22 records...Lee told Chapter to fuck off! At the time his sister had died in an accident on a horse and he sat at her gravestone drinking 'OI! God! Why did you kill my sister, you cunt!' The band could have been big; they got more support slots with The Alarm and Spear of Destiny but Lee just told A and R men to fuck off. Why? That's another good question. His state of mind, his punk ethics or something else?

The band got another chance. After a gig in Brum a big record company guy offered to sign them. This was it! But the guy drank Lee's beer and he said, 'Listen, cunt, nobody drinks my beer.' The guy left; they signed the Cult instead. The band signed for a minor label and got some cash, but it went the usual rock and roll route. After getting a thousand pound payment and two days in London and breaking his cock (did you know you can break your cock?) he arrived back in Kiddy, with a mic stand and some great stories although fairly blurred.

The band fell apart; two of its members, brothers, later committed suicide. Was the cost of failure to become famous the cause?

I had been in a few bands myself but got sidetracked by politics and travel and adventure. But, Lee's dream was to make it, so he trudged on!

He formed the Ice Babies and became part of the Soho Rock, glam sleaze scene. And this band went more commercial, Lee really went for it, to finally make that breakthrough. And that scene was a wild scene of late night clubs and early morning bars and coke and groupies and orgies. And that band split and White Trash was formed again a record deal was got and support to Lords of the New Church and Hanoi Rocks followed as did even more debauchery on the road and around Soho.

And the women came; Angie Bowie and then Jane Dickenson ex-wife of Iron Maiden's singer. She took Lee to LA where they indulged in drug and drink fuelled nights with car crashes and head bashes and waking up with cowboy boots and a hat in a bath after a threesome.

The LA scene was toxic, guns and toots and boozing and loots.

The band broke up and a broken Lee left to save himself and went with a penniless Spanish girl and moved to Zaragoza. He drifted into the Gypsy Barrios and mixed it with flamenco guitarists and gangsters and formed a new band, The Last Gang. Tours followed supporting the Ramones and Motorhead. They got thrown off the Ramones tour for doing Pistols' covers after being asked not to.

And coke and speed filled nights with Lemmy and his Jack, until he got pissed and told him to 'Get rid of that fucking wart, you cunt!'

So, back to the UK and White Trash UK was formed and Lee got the closet yet to signing a major deal. One hour before the guy who was about to sign them, he lost control of the company. More tours followed with big bands and fights with Slash and more drugs and groupies. Living the rock and roll lifestyle mannnn! They had a minor record deal and radio play and MTV appearances but again didn't quite make the top.

The music business is a rigged game. And Lee for some reason tried to play the game but something always bugged him enough to fuck it up just at the wrong moment. His punk ideals? His just fucking stupidity or again was there something else underneath the surface going on?

Then in 2003 the last roll of the dice! The Gypsy Pistoleros...they got an instant tribal, loyal following.

The sound was flamenco in a head on collision with punk/rock riffs, pounding bass and thrashing drums. The songs span madly in the best rock 'n' roll tradition! With big hooks, attitude, and sleaze. Yet those flamenco breaks got into your head and refused to leave.

This mongrel offspring of fiery flamenco passion and gritty gutter glam, the Gypsy Pistoleros were born roamin' somewhere between Barcelona and Birmingham, brought into the world to a soundtrack stack-heeled anthems of sleazy seventies America. Standing alone in musical ancestry and slum sound, they were one of those most rare acts who honestly could claim the tag 'unique'.

They headlined at festivals in the US and made a few albums. Again never really making it mega big but big enough I think. Then there were splits and conflicts and Lee took up acting appearing in a few minor B movies and some great theatre productions. This culminated in his 30-day one man show at the Edinburgh Festival. A rock and roll suicide. A big hit.

In the meantime he was diagnosed with ADHD and a borderline personality disorder.

The questions arise; are these diagnosis what made him fuck things up or the things that enabled him to do so much? I believe they are just a part of his personality, maybe they made him be a rock and roller for forty odd years; made him able to get up on that stage whether singing or acting. Did he fuck things up? Yeah of course but that was part of the punk spirit that lived in him. Did he make it? Yeah, of course he did...he performed for years, doing something he loved and believed in. But he never made it famous? What is fame? And who gives a fuck anyway...he did what a lot of us punks did...he got himself out of the shithole direction that our lives were destined to follow. Did his disorders fuck him up or his chances of fame? Maybe, but then again so what? The Pistoleros have reformed have a new album out and are gigging again, not a final throw of the dice but a continuation of a spirit; living life his way and to the full and living the punk dream. Born a rocker die and rocker.

Giv'us a Lift, Mate!

'You do yours, I'll do mine. I'll just pull over, no funny business like.' This was the driver; I was hitching from Brum to Derby. 'Yeah, me and my mates often have a wank together, you know we're not gay or anything, just a good laugh!'

I wasn't laffing, I'd only been in the car for half an hour and it was late, I didn't wanna get out, there weren't many cars on the road. 'No, you're alright, mate, I'll just get out up here.'

In the late seventies and the whole of the eighties I hitchhiked everywhere. Often to get to see bands, the train was too dear, and I'd been caught too often bunking it. There were a lot of hitchers in those days, funny you don't see many now? Everyone is scared of weirdoes, but back then weirdoes were par for the course. I was always getting offers and caresses on my legs. One guy offered me thirty quid for sex and forty if I kept my leather jacket on. Another guy, they always seemed to be salesmen too, offered to take me to a room and he wanted me to eat an orange in my underpants, for a tenner, while he jerked off! Go figure!

There were notorious roads for weirdoes, known by the hitching fraternity. The A34 Oxford to Northampton road was one of them; I had been felt up many a time on there. Two punkettes I knew told me the story of one hitch they did. They were going to Northampton to see a gig at the Roadmenders. On the way there they got in the back and with their knives in their bags felt kinda safe. After a while this guy pulls over, comes round the side window and proceeded to take his togger out and start masturbating. After the gig, the girls stayed the night on some mate's floor and in the morning hit the A34 again to get home. Some businessman gave them a lift and after a while looked at them in the rear-view mirror and asked, 'You don't mind if I have a wank do you?' And whilst looking at the girls in the mirror and still driving, had a wank.

Hitchers were full of these stories, but it never really deterred us and no one got harmed, it went with the territory really.

My girlfriend and me hitched from Paris to Barcelona and got a great lift off a lorry driver, almost all the way. But lorry drivers liked to talk dirty, they never made moves like stroking legs, and were never into any gay stuff, but they liked it blue!

'So, yeah I go down to the nudist beach and park up take me binoculars out and watch, I love watching people in the noddy, know what I mean? If you wanna you two can get it together in the back here, I'll just watch, no funny business!' We got to Barcelona without having had to have sex in the cab.

Of course there were some great lifts too. One woman gave about five of us a lift and fed us and put us up in her cottage for the night. Others bought you breakfast or fags, and some went out of their way to get you to where you wanted to go.

As I said there were well known roads for pervs. But also well known spots for getting good lifts. You jumped the Tube to Brent Cross on the outskirts of London and walked to the layby to the motorways going North and usually you only waited about ten minutes and got a lift easily.

We had a code amongst the hitchers you always stood behind the guy who was there before you or you asked them where they wanting you to stand. Anyone who pushed in was given a mouthful and some were forced to stand at the back when they wouldn't move. Yeah, there were some great roads but apart from the pervy roads there were infamous places where it was nigh on impossible to get a lift from; the most famous of these was Gordano services on the motorway near Bristol. The graffiti on the barriers on the slip road read 'Hitchhikers graveyard' and there were skeletons with backpacks lined up along the side of the road. I was there for two days once; people just didn't give you a lift. And if you were heading down the west side of the country you asked the lift before you got in, to make sure they weren't gonna drop you at Gordano and disappear into Bristol.

One of my longest hitches was from the top of old Yugoslavia to Athens. We had been on one of the islands in Croatia and got a boat to the mainland. On the map there was a clear route down towards Albania on a coast road then take a right to Thessaloniki then a straight run to Athens. The coast road was a bit desolate and not much traffic. I was with my mate Gal and we tried to hitch together but after five hours decided it would be better to split up. We both had a little cash on us and we spilt it up evenly, we had travellers' cheques but made a bet that we weren't allowed to cash any till we got to Athens.

I waved him off after an hour then stuck my thumb out. I got a lift off a great guy who stopped in a village and bought me lunch, so with my cash I bought some fags for the journey, food I could do without and scrounge from punters but fags I needed. After a day's hitching I got dropped near some industrial estate and decided to sleep till the morning, rounding a safe corner of a warehouse there was Gal! He had spent his cash on a bottle of vodka and some food, so we shared our goods and got some sleep. We departed separately the next morning and again got lifts pretty easily. After a long day of hitching I got dumped on the wrong side of a town so walked to the other side to the road leading south, there on the side of the road again was Gal. We were delighted to see each other again and decided to sleep until morning. We found some allotments and stole some fruit and got chased by a big dog. There was an empty shack on the side of the road, a kiosk kinda thing, and we forced open the back door and after eating and smoking we got our heads down. The next day we departed again. And I headed further south. I was stuck on the side of a main road with the coast on one side and holiday traffic everywhere, there were no good hitching places so I walked to try and find one, with my thumb out as I walked. All the cars were full of holiday makers and their gear so I got no lifts. Then a little Citroen passed me and then reversed. It was packed full of all sorts of junk and a nice woman said she was going to Prizren; this was a good lift, a long way, I got in eagerly. She was Swiss and after half an hour of conversation I found out she was off to visit her Albanese boyfriend at his home, he didn't know she was coming and the more she talked the more I realised what a nutter she was. I wanted to get out but the thought of such a long lift kept me inside. The first night we parked up on top of some small mountain and draped over each other got some kip. She kept stopping all the time to talk to locals and buy shit off people selling at the side of the road. Once into Kosovo we entered another world it was like going back a hundred years. Peasants walked with drooped backs carrying bales of firewood and farmers watched us with their pitchforks and she waved and hooted the horn. I started to get really angry with her and at one point told her to stop the bloody car and leave me here. Thankfully after an hour she came back for me and I reluctantly got back in. There were some kids in a forest selling local artefacts, she pulled over and swapped some of her shit for the goods. We drove on, only to be met in the road by a gang of angry pitchfork wielding adults who stopped the car and gave her her shit back and got their artefacts back off her, they wanted money not tat. Eventually we got to Prizren. And she picked up every little kid on the road so I was forced to sit on top of the sunroof holding a bloody guitar. We arrived into the main square where a crowd of angry locals were gathered and guns were shooting bullets through the air. What a sight we must have looked in the middle of a rebellion, a crazy Swiss woman with a sunburnt English guy on the roof with a guitar and a car full of shit and kids. We found the boyfriend's house. He wasn't there. And the family had never heard of her, she started to move her shit into the house and talking crazily. The daughter translated and when she said the mother was a seamstress she dropped her pants and asked her if she could fix her undies. The look from the mother and the father of this strict Muslim family sent daggers through the air. I was getting worried. We were invited for dinner, kidneys and potatoes, and I was offered a shower which I took and a bed for the night which I refused. I was very polite and the mother liked me and gave me a medallion of Prizren silver. But I insisted in being given a lift to the road out of town, I could see trouble round the corner. And the mother nodded in understanding. They packed me some food and left me at the edge of town, where I got into my sleeping bag and happily went to sleep. I often wonder what happened to the Swiss woman, something horrible I hope. It took me five days to get to Athens, cashed my cheque and waited to meet Gal under the Acropolis at 11 every day. After two days we met up. I had beat him by a day and he had caved in at Titograd had cashed his cheque got some grub and a haircut and got a lift with the Yugoslavian army most of the way.

As I said before some places were just not good for hitching from and at the end of the eighties I gave up my hitching life. I had been dropped at Gordano and am now married with three kids and living in Bristol!

The King of the Baboons, I presume

My wife and I had lived sparsely on the lake for six months. We ran a real eco-tourist lodge. No electric, no proper sewerage, no communication apart from a Roberts shortwave radio which we listened to for the BBC; African news, football on a Saturday whilst I watched a local village match; and best of all on a Sunday afternoon, when all the workers were off, I cooked a nice chicken we had caught on the open fire and we sat on the decking looking out over the lake listening to *War of the Worlds*.

Having no transport meant little travel was done apart from expeditions to Mzuzu to buy supplies and to get drunk at the ex-pats bar and to wolf down sausage sandwiches with our beers and tales.

Local transport was usually on open-back Matolas; open-back pickup trucks. Sometimes a national bus would appear but not often. There were also sporadic minibuses. All of them were unreliable and dangerously over-loaded; we feared for our lives whilst squeezed against a big woman's bosom whilst trying to stop a monkey from eating our food.

Along the lake were many mission stations. These had been started by Dr Livingstone. He had started them then had moved on; trying to stop his fellow missionaries from dying of malaria. Eventually, he founded the small town and mission of Livingstonia, up a 900-metre-high escarpment, far enough away from the mosquitoes. We decided to take some time off and go on an adventure; to try to get to Livingstonia by public transport, or to be honest by any means we could!

After a day of wild rides we got dropped at the stop from where you get a ride or walk up to the mission. There was nothing at the stop except a hut and a guy selling a few goods; fags, bread rolls, gum and Powers vodka shots; and snippets of travel information; he didn't know much. He said you can walk or wait for a Matola; there maybe one coming soon. With the heat, we decided to wait and had a few smokes, and a few shots of Powers to loosen the time. There were about seven other people there, all with large bags of food or cloth or chairs. After two hours a Matola arrived. It was already pretty full but we flashed some cash again and got slung in the back amongst the bodies and bags of goods and live chickens. It took three hours to climb up. Very often at some very steep curves we all got off and pushed the bloody thing.

We finally made it up. Livingstonia was a Scottish village somehow whisked from the Highlands to the highlands of Malawi. There were red brick houses and a school; the kids wore school uniforms and came from far and wide. We looked at old photos of missionaries being carried on chairs on locals' shoulders. We dusted ourselves off and went to the hotel for tea in china cups and fairy cakes and triangular sandwiches of fish paste. It was lovely and weird at the same time. We inspected the hospital and spoke to some American doctor and got the obligatory malaria test. We enjoyed our visit I suppose; it was nice to visit a part of Scotland. But it was not Africa and we decided to not spend the night. There was no way down by motor so with the advice of the doctor, we decided to climb down. We were told not to follow the roads but just to head straight down through the bush. It was hard going down the sharp inclines and we had to force ourselves not to run too fast.

My wife was a student of photography, having just done a course and purchased a good camera. She stopped now and then to take photos. Suddenly we heard a series of grunts and barks and yaks and wahoos coming from the forest. Down the side of the bush we came down to a roadway, and I saw some small animals sitting on a wall. I moved closer and saw that they were small baboons. My wife was offering crumbled biscuits in her out-stretched hand; these were the quaint babies.

She took out her camera and walked further to get a close-up. From behind me, the yelps were getting louder and more spread out; and worst of all...nearer.

Suddenly baboons started to jump up onto the road. They were springing up like the skeletons from a *Jason and the Argonauts* film, and were spreading out in a state of panic, for some reason.

-Come back to me! Slowly!

She didn't seem to grasp the seriousness of our situation at first then with the force of my pull she got it. We stood still and they seemed to ignore us, something was scaring them and they were on the run. They bounced up the hill and then another troop came over the walls, these were the guys making the loudest noises. We realised we were in the middle of a fight. They bounced over the wall and slowly came past us suspiciously. Then I spotted him. On a rock overlooking the proceedings was a huge specimen of baboonhood. He sat chest out and turned his head all around slowly. He looked like a king on his thrown. Then he let out huge barks, orders to his troops. He looked at me, right between the eyes, and stared.

-I think we had better move.

We edged along the road, head and shoulders bowed, looking up quickly to see his stare following us. Once we were far enough away he let out a huge growl and the troops scattered up the hill after the other troop. When they had all advanced he climbed down from the rock and as I turned back he stopped, looked at us, seemed to nod, and slowly turned his head and elegantly galloped up the escarpment.

Stand your Ground

Then you progress...you move further to the back, you buy the boots and wrap the scarf round your wrist and go stand with the bigger guys at the back who lead the chanting. Then after the game you follow them as they go looking for the away fans...along the road as their mob are led along the road to Smethwick Rolfe street station. The big guys try and get at their big guys; you tag along behind; trying to look tough. When the police are not around or running disorganised with their dogs the real fighting starts and both sets of hooligans look for each other; sometimes one gang runs at another. 'Stand your ground' and you stand, you don't run. You look for some guys the same size as you and you aim a punch or a kick.

Most of it is bravado. But as you progress to away games you get involved more, you start to run with the big guys and beat people up and also get beaten yourself; smacks in the mouth are shocking at first then you get used to them. Kicked to the ground and getting laid into is always scary. It wasn't always like this...

You started as a fan. Young kid with all the scarves, rosettes, jumpers and a bobble hat. I went with my granddad who had had the bug passed onto him from his dad and granddad and back it goes. This is your team! Take 'um for what they are...they are yours! And that's it; you are stuck for life with a crap team who never wins anything. Sixty-eight was the last cup we won. My granddad said he jumped up and landed five rows of seats down; and didn't get home to Birmingham for a couple of days. He never said what he got up to.

We stood behind the goal and if we couldn't see, which was often the case, the crowd passed the kids over their heads down the front, where you squeezed your face through the railings to catch a glimpse. We mostly saw the goalie who was a character, John Osborne. He goofed around and chatted to the crowd when the action was up the other end. He always placed his false teeth at the side of the post before the game and when he could scrounged a fag off someone and leant on the post and puffed away. I remember him losing them one time in the mud; we all howled while he searched around his goal-mouth on his hands and knees.

We loved those piss-drenched terraces. We loved the colours...the pitch always seemed too green, the scarves too blue, like a vivid avant-garde painting. We took it all in; the swearing, the chants, the banter and loved it all. We got caught up in the humour, the passion, and the euphoria.

As you got older you moved towards the back, away from your granddad and nearer the cool guys who sang; and then I changed ends to be with the even cooler guys who fought. We stood next to the away fans and threw insults and sharpened coins.

After I left him I would meet up with my granddad at half time behind the stands and he would give me a still warm wrapped package of sausage and tomato sandwich with brown sauce from my nan. We chatted a little. 'Not getting into any trouble I hope?' he quizzed me and smiled as he knew. Maybe he had done the same, I bet he did. I heard there was fighting even in the fifties especially when we paid Villa; and I knew he hated them fiercely, and the away day to Villa was the highlight of his season. He got so wound up; I could imagine him and his mates fighting in the Witton Road after the games in the fifties, with their Teddy boy haircuts and razor knives. I heard there had been fighting before then too; maybe a more sophisticated form of hooliganism. I imagine a crowd making a circle and two men would take off their jackets and with flat caps on take up Queensbury rules stances as the fans urged them on.

But I earned my stripes at a big ruck. We had been to Middlesbrough three years before and only a few coaches and mini vans had made it. We were surrounded in the ground and got kicked and punched throughout the game and the cops watched and when we complained they said, 'You shouldn't have fucking come up here then!'

As we tried to sneak out we got followed. I had five guys, all my age about sixteen, put me against a wall and kick the shit out of me, and robbed my pockets, and took my coat. I wasn't the worst off either. The next year a van of some of our heavy boys went up early and attacked one of their pubs. Chrisy Bates got thirty stitches down his back.

So, this was the time for revenge. Some of the guys from the pub fight were there along with some slightly older bigger guys brought in from the factories in donkey jackets. There were about twenty-five of us and we got the thirty-minute train up to the ground early. Scarves were put down trousers to protect your bollocks from a kicking and no other colours were worn. The plan was to go into the away end where we expected some of their main men to be. There weren't too many coppers about and we staggered through the turnstiles nonchalantly and gathered under the stand near the burger guy before entering up the steps to the bottom of the terrace. All in, we moved in. We walked up the stairs and looked up. Along the top of the terrace were about a hundred guys, who all stopped and looked down. It was obvious who we were and they had been waiting for us. We hadn't expected so many of them and we all stood silently for a moment and stared; my heart and arsehole were pumping. Shit!

Then there came a cry and the one hundred came piling down. Our guys spread out and the old guys cried, 'Stand your ground!' I stood behind a barrier and waited for the avalanche to arrive. I was lost in the kicking and punching but managed to land a few good ones back too. We got fucked but we never ran. Some of our donkey jacket guys were laying guys out one after another, Chrisy Bates, the guy who was knifed, took on five on his own. We retreated whilst we fought back under the stand and the cops pinned us behind the burger guy. Then the one hundred stood in front of us and hurled insults and provocation and we did the same back; it was easy now with the cops in the way. Then we were led through the crowd into our own fans' section to applause and cheers.

We were heroes, we hadn't run, we had took them on and gave a good account of ourselves. Hands were shaken, backs were slapped. We had stood our ground and that was the most important thing.

Just a Peach Schnapps Kiss

-You need to move to Brno, my friend.

This was a psychiatrist in Vyskov who I was seeing because of my alcohol problems. Basically, I was drinking my face off. What else was there to do here? A soldiers' town with a few bars and two shit discos with bad strippers. I had come here from Birmingham via Lisbon where, after two years of hedonism, I had cried out for help from someone to set me up somewhere else. So, I ended up here working and living in an agricultural school. My room was next to my classroom, and sometimes the students had to come in and wade through the bottles and books and pizza boxes to wake me up to teach them.

-Really, you think that might help?

-If you stay here you may die!

Fair enough, I'll move then. So I did.

Someone lent me a flat but I wasn't allowed to use it. I had no electric or gas or furniture, so it was just a place to crash. My drinking didn't stop; I found the worst bars and took my lunch of cheap soup and cheap beer amongst the alcos in the train station bar. I got some work, so started to go to better bars like The Hobbit and The Two Goats, where there were cool young people, so I behaved myself more and tried to get to know people; well, women to be honest.

The guy who owned the flat gave me two weeks to get out after I set my mattress on fire after a bender. I had fallen asleep with a fag in my mouth but thought I had put it out and put it smouldering onto the balcony and went back to my drunken slumber. I got woke up again by the fire brigade banging on the door and rubbed my eyes to see the bed blazing away on the balcony. So, I had to get out.

It wasn't easy to find flats back in '95, I asked around and got a job in a language school and put an advert up...Room wanted! I got no replies. And I asked every class I had if anyone had a room to rent. I got no interested faces.

One day a colleague was sick so I had to cover for him. At the front of the class was this interesting-looking woman; huge rolled-up jumper and flared trousers and mad jewellery, and short hair. She stood out amongst the mini-skirted high-heeled, big bouffant hair brigade.

So, I spent the lesson trying to engage a lot with her, but she just flipped me off with 'yes' and 'no' answers, so I gave up. During the lesson I did my usual pitch about needing a room, after the class the girl approached me.

-I have a room you can rent.

-Really? That's great.

-I share a panelak with three guys, we are all croupiers, so we are not there much, but you could rent the living room.

-OK, that sounds fine.

-Just one thing, you'll have to share the room with Kevin.

-Who's Kevin?

-Kevin's our rat.

-Is he a friendly rat?

-Yeah very friendly, but we don't keep him in a cage, I mean when I say share, you really will be sharing.

-Well, I've shared rooms with worse people than rats, I'll take it.

-Here's the address you can move in today, here's a key, I'll be home about nine, after my shift.

So, I moved my stuff in and made some food and waited for the strangers who I would be living with. The three guys arrived about seven. All cool guys, into good music, though too much metal for my liking, and sports and drinking. We got to know each other over shots of Slivovice and some beers.

Dasa arrived at nine with a bottle of peach Schnapps. We retreated to my room, the living room and Kevin's place of residence. We had a good chat, though her English wasn't that good as she spent a lot of time in the pub with a gang of suitors who followed her around all the time, I was to find out. With the bottle nearly empty she leaned in and whispered...

-Would you mind if I kissed you?

-Not at all.

We kissed, not too deeply, but it was a good kiss.

And that was it; we went to bed, separately.

The next day at school I told the guy who I had substituted for that the move seemed great! I got drunk and a kiss from my landlady.

After some classes Dasa and her gang of guys approached me.

-Don't ever talk about what I do out of school understand?

-Yeah sure, sorry about that.

She went off in a huff. The teacher had mentioned the kissing and drinking in his class and she was well pissed off. I went home and she was aloof and abrupt with me. I thought that this was a big mistake and was going to be a nightmare place to live in; what with this stuck-up housemate.

She continued to be aloof and snobbish, and I started to really detest her and dreaded going home to be in the same flat as her. The guys were OK though, and we went to pubs, and to see Boby Brno play.

Things changed after a few weeks when I lost my job because I wasn't turning up for work because of hangovers. Dasa then shaved her head and consequently lost her job too.

Here we both were, jobless, skint and stuck in the same house as each other; nightmare!

-I am going to a new art exhibition if you want to come?

-Sure, why not.

And actually, we had a good time; we went for a coffee after and chatted and got on OK, not best buddies but OK.

In the next few weeks, we went to loads of different places; hidden gardens, museums and our favourite art house cinemas. In Lisen amongst the rows of panelaks was a shopping centre and in the middle of it was a cinema restaurant. This was a great place to see a film.

The tables had comfy sofas and chairs and all raised a little higher so everyone got a good view. They bought steaks and wine to our table as we watched *Frankenstein* and *Natural Born Killers*.

Over those weeks we began to get to know each other better and started to like each other more. I had thought she was a stuck-up snob, and she thought me an arrogant over-confident dick. But spending time together we changed our views, I saw she was an intelligent, funny and caring woman, and I think she thought the same of me. After one night out we ended up in bed together and from there our relationship blossomed. We spent loads of time together and eventually, we both got new jobs. And I used to watch her walk to work or come back from work through the window and I adored watching her walking in that red coat. Gradually, over time, we fell in love with each other, and we became a couple.

Our usual route after being in town was the number two tram to Zidenice then a trolley bus up the hill to the rabbit hutches of Vinohrady. In the shopping area, there was a bar that stayed open all night. It wasn't a cosy bar; a lot of metal and Formica, and terrible music played on a tinny tape player. So, not that pleasant but always good for a couple before bed.

One night we arrived late or early according to the clock and went in for one; it was never one. This night the place was empty apart from two guys at the bar. One was really short and the other a big bear of a man. We stood at the bar to drink and started chatting. Turned out it was the grizzle's birthday. So, the drinks flowed as we celebrated with them. The midget guy spoke English so I stood chatting with him while Dasa was left with the drunken ramblings of the bear. She was sat on a stool and he leaned in more and more as he got more and more drunk. I asked him politely to stop getting in her face so much but with little effect. In the end, I got pissed off and warned the midget that if his brother didn't stop bothering Dasa then I would smack him one. But, this guy kept leaning in and leaning in.

-Look, man! I won't ask him again. Tell him to back the fuck off or there's going to be trouble.

-It's cool, man, calm down, I'll tell him; he will be fine.

After another five minutes, he wasn't fine at all, in fact worse. I got off my stool walked behind him and tapped his shoulder and as he turned I smacked him one, a right beauty, right under his nose.

He fell to the floor. Suddenly, the dwarf was on my back, punching anywhere he could. I rolled over and over with this guy on my back and we smashed a couple of tables flat as we rolled. Next, the bear got up and dived in. Now, I had two of them punching and rolling and flattening every table in the place.

Meanwhile, the waitress had called the cops and they arrived and pulled us all apart. The waitress then explained that it was all mine and Dasa's fault for the whole thing; the place was a wreck.

So, me and Dasa got handcuffed and thrown into the back of a meat wagon.

At the cop shop, we were searched and had our shoes taken away and thrown into a cell. At least they let us smoke, and we sat there still drunk contemplating what would happen. Dasa was worried; me not so much, it wasn't my first cell visit.

After a while, we were led into an interview room with a guy behind a typewriter at a desk. He was wobbling a bit and had clearly been drinking; shots of Slivovice behind his locker door no doubt.

-So, you started the fight in the bar.

-Wait a minute!

The guy rolled off statement after statement where we were said to be the sole perpetrators of the fight.

-Sign here!

-No way, I am English and I don't understand anything and demand a translator.

Dasa translated for me. She spoke firmly and it seemed to have the right effect. Things got serious all of a sudden and we were put back into our cell. We were there for some hours until we were taken again to an office and had a guy read the statement to me in English. We refused to sign it and we dictated our own statement denying everything.

After a couple more hours in the cells, we were given a load of paperwork and our shoes and let go.

It was almost midday. And we now had hangovers and had not slept. What to do? We went to the nearest bar for a beer and to think things over. For some reason, I really fancied some Chinese, so we hopped a few trams to our favourite restaurant that was just opening. It was Dasa's first time drinking in the morning and she went with the flow. We drank a few bottles and wolfed down some food and started to feel better. Her initial shock and fear started to disappear a little. We took a tram and had some drinks at the terminus, took the trolley bus up the hill, fucked quickly, and at last went to sleep.

A couple of days later the Midget and the Gorilla appeared with a cop at the door, their brother-in-law. They gave us a warning that things could get very difficult for us, but with some cash paid, it could all go away.

They came a couple of more times and the guys in the flat said I needed to pay these guys or I might have to go to court or even get done over by the cops; or even, both!

I looked at my options; part with cash was not an option, and hope for fair justice was not on offer either.

-I think I should get the hell out of here.

The guys agreed; with me out of the way Dasa wouldn't get into any trouble.

In the Two Goats, I told Dasa.

-It's our only option.

-I'll come with you.

-You'll come to England with me? To live? That would be great. I mean you'll have to give me some time to get set it up, you know, somewhere to live, a job and that.

-Nick, I know you by now. It's not going to be easy but it's definitely going to be interesting.

A week later I packed my bag and took a rickety old bus to London.

After a few months, I was set up with a job in Cambridge and a room in a shared house, so Dasa packed her bag and got the same rickety bus and we hugged each other deeply in Victoria coach station before taking the train to Cambridge and beyond.

Thievery in a time of quarantine

I mean I can't claim benefits! Question: occupation... burglar! I don't think they'll pay out do you? So, what can a burglar do in a time of virus lockdown? It's the second week and this is the question I am asking myself. Everybody's at home for god's sake!

So desperate times call for desperate measures right? Here in Czech you can't cross the borders, cos I was thinking about the Austrian weekend cottages, they are bound to have loads of valuable goods. Last weekend I went up to a Czech cottage area. Got into a few; easily done. But they've got fuck all! Old boots, sandals, jars of cherries and jams, bottles of slivovice, which I took obviously, but nothing of value. Old portable black and white TVs, and even video machines, I mean, Jesus, who is going to buy one of those? No plasma TVs, no laptops. Just wardrobes of old clothes and stacks of slippers and smoked meats hanging from hooks.

No, cottages are out!

Cars! Break into cars. Now usually this is my fall back method of income. People are always in a hurry and leave laptops and purses inside the cars. But no one is going anywhere, so no one is leaving anything in the cars. Packets of gum and a chocolate bar with a bite out of it, and hiking boots! I could steal the car but no one is buying and the borders are closed.

Shops! No panic buying here so the shops have everything.

Cafés and restaurants are useless...who wants to buy a second-hand deep fat fryer?

Hold on, hold on! Hipster cafés! Yes!

I break into one and realise that they have trendy coffee cups and those fashionable jug things for takeaway; and, and espresso machines. I phone a mate and we manage to get one out and into the back of the van. I set up an account on eBay and sell hipster café shit for the home!

So, please don't worry about me. I am managing alright. Money coming in. Staying safe, loving the masks! I can't help feel a bit sorry for the pickpockets though. How the hell they gonna manage?

Well, if we have to...

-For fuck's sake let's just get married!

Not the most romantic of proposals I'll grant you, the setting was no better either; being in a cell at the detention centre at Heathrow airport.

My girlfriend had been deported for the second time. The first time had been at the ferry port when they had checked her diary and seen *Work Monday, Tuesday etc.* She was no holiday maker but an illegal alien. She lost her passport, I sent money for a flight but the bloody computer age put paid to her sneaking back in.

Hence, here we were in the centre pissed off with the whole thing.

She said yes of course, and we did want to be together; we just both of us, had never wanted to do the whole wedding thing.

So, after a few months I got to Prague and we had our meeting with the British embassy. We spent all night in a hotel going through every scenario; if it was an old Stalinist bag, what would we say? If she was too nice, trying to trick us, what response to give?

Like *Green Card* the movie, we were interviewed, and sailed through; we knew enough about each other for them to see we were the real thing. There was some snotty English business guy there, full of confidence, and a blonde gold digger on his arm. He thought his school tie would get him through. I threw a smirk at him and waved our papers when he left the room, head down, the blonde waving away his hand.

So we got in! We had to be married within six months. So we booked Cambridge registry office at the earliest available date.

We thought we would maybe just have a few friends and our mums and dads there, but once we starting talking to the mums they began to get all weddingy on us; gotta have a cake, and a video, that kind of thing. So, we told them all we wouldn't have anyone; just us and two witnesses.

We sought out something appropriate to wear in the second-hand shops. I got a grey Russian suit and Dasa got a 1920s white dress; perfect.

On the morning of the day, I thought we should get into the swing of things a little. I poured some cocaine into the champagne bottle and we drank it for breakfast. My mate from work was one witness, turned up in a jacket and jumper. The other was the landlord of the pub opposite the office, where Dasa worked. We met there at 9 and had a few drinks. We were both flying by now and with big grins on our faces we made our way across the road. The people doing the ceremony were very serious and got very annoyed as we giggled our way through the ceremony. Making us take photos of an empty congregation. We came out killing ourselves laughing and went back to the pub where we were joined by a few more friends. After a lot of drink we decided to head into town to eat, and score some more coke. We got some and sat chugging wine and eating lamb kebabs in our favourite Turkish restaurant. We hit the pub next door to drink with more mates. Early evening we headed home to change. The friends we shared the house with hit us with a cake and more wine. By eightish I was too hammered to do anything and they put me to bed; spark out. Dasa and the guys decided to go clubbing, lesbian and gay night at the Junction. And that's how we spent our wedding night, her getting picked up by women, me comatose. Our life after kind of followed the mood of that day, but we have been together over twenty years, so all in all not a bad thing.

Goodbye Mr Gargoyle.

A lament to my friend Tony who took his own life just before the release of this book.

A joker, nun or jester standing tall amongst beer bellies, navies or studded youth

An original amongst men he never let his artistic aspirations fester.

Standing out from a crowd, being a face first there.

Together we robbed safes, cars and pickled jars and sold old furniture and rented our rooms for beer.

You dared step wherever was forbidden.

And you made me laugh so much and there are stories that must remain forever hidden

Your sense of style was like no one else, you are in the book of new romantics, first before Steve strange.

I was happy you found love at last and spent your last years so happy. Even though the habit you wore was no longer a nun's

You were cooler then the coolest guys. You shunned fashion and fame cuss you disliked the shoes.

I giggled and lied with you, I fought with you, we tricked and treated, did good and cheated.

We ran from cops, we pilfered shops, we went first class and went on the lash

In dingy Irish pubs in Digbeth to selling t shirts in Camden, it was all a gas.

You were a one in a million, my mate, my companion.

You stood out and dared to be different. And I'll remember super gluing the locks to stop the city and trashing a Rolls Royce just cuss it was there.

And now you are gone my mate. My books are full of you. My life is fuller because I knew you.

I loved you back then and I love you still. I am proud of you and miss you. Good bye and stay free

My friend

A. Gargoyle still written on the envelope of the dole cheque.

Milton Keynes UK
Ingram Content Group UK Ltd.
UKHW011814120624
444110UK00001B/55

9 798227 197085